THE STATIN CONTROVERSY

AND HOW TO RESOLVE IT

Geoffrey Galley

Published by

MELROSE
BOOKS

An Imprint of Melrose Press Limited
St Thomas Place, Ely
Cambridgeshire
CB7 4GG, UK
www.melrosebooks.co.uk

FIRST EDITION

Copyright © Geoffrey Galley 2018

The Author asserts his moral right to
be identified as the author of this work

Cover designed by Jeremy Kay

ISBN   978-1-912333-69-1 paperback
       978-1-912333-70-7 epub
       978-1-912333-71-4 mobi

Printed and bound in Great Britain by:
CPI Group (UK) Ltd, Croydon, CR0 4YY

An Introduction to the Book and the Author
By Uffe Ravnskov

For more than three decades, a controversy has raged between the pharmaceutical companies, the health services and independent doctors and scientists over the use of statin drugs. It affects the health of millions of members of the public who are increasingly confused by conflicting arguments over the safety and efficacy of the drugs which are already prescribed for over 7 million people in the UK.

On the one hand the pharmaceutical companies tell us that lowering our cholesterol with statins reduces the number of fatal and non-fatal heart attacks and strokes with relatively few harmless side effects. The healthcare services agree with this assessment and expect statin use to save many millions of pounds in reduced costs of care and treatment of those suffering from heart disease. On the other hand, hundreds of doctors and medical research scientists claim that the benefits of the drugs are exaggerated and the harms are grossly understated. They argue that the harms caused by statins far exceed the benefits and that in the long term the costs incurred in dealing with the consequences of statin treatment will exceed any savings from delayed deaths and cardiovascular events. Most importantly, many express the view that statins will result in increased infirmity in the elderly.

Geoffrey Galley, the author of this booklet, has stepped into the middle of this seemingly unresolvable dispute and provided us with a remarkable solution which should be equally attractive to those on both sides of the argument. Instead of accepting what would be an unmanageable adjudication of the vast body of scientific and technical information underpinning the case made by each side, he proposes an independent retrospective review of the state of health and level of survival of a significant number of individuals who have been treated with statins over a period of between ten and 20 years as compared with individuals with the same initial risk factors as the statin takers who have not received statin treatment.

This he argues will quickly reveal answers to all the important questions which will either lead to the increased use of statins urged by the pharmaceutical companies and the healthcare services or will signal the need to end statin treatment for those who face increasing damage to their health through continued use of the drugs.

In my view it is a brilliant proposal as it will provide indisputable evidence of the safety and efficacy of the drugs in daily use over a lengthy period of years in contrast to the widely differing clinical and research evaluations of statin performance provided by a multitude of different sources.

It is interesting to note that the author is not a medically trained doctor but he is a scientist trained in the principles of scientific analysis with a Bachelor's degree in applied physics and a Master's degree in operational research. He has used his skills to look into the subject of cardiovascular disease and present the two sides of the argument in a lucid exposition that can be easily read and understood by the layman. He is also a successful entrepreneur with significant achievements in the field of contact lens manufacture, where his company won the Queen's Award for Industry and in the field of aviation where an aircraft developed by another of his companies flew at the Farnborough Airshow. In addition he has been involved in research projects in the field of cancer treatment and non-invasive measurement of cardiovascular disease.

As well as setting out the arguments advanced by those involved in the statin controversy in the clearest terms, he has provided historical information about the role of cholesterol in heart disease, early investigations into the causes of heart disease and the underlying explanation for the 20th century epidemic of deaths from heart attacks which started in the 1930s, reached a peak in 1970 and then began a continual decline long before statin drugs reached the market. There is also an enlightening chapter on the biochemistry of the statins which explains why the anti-statin lobby is so concerned about the long-term effects of treatment with this drug.

An important element of his proposed solution is to bring the matter before the members of the UK Parliament whom he sees as the only body with the power to initiate an independent and unbiased review of statin treatment, free from the influence of the pharmaceutical companies and the healthcare services, both of which have an overwhelming financial interest in the issue.

In my view his impressive and informative booklet has a real chance of resolving a dispute which has far-reaching effects on the long-term health of a significant percentage of the UK population.

Uffe Ravnskov MD PhD
Author of *The Cholesterol Myths* and spokesperson for the International Network of Cholesterol Skeptics. (http://www.thincs.org)

Foreword

At present in the UK over 7 million people are taking statins to lower their cholesterol in the belief that this will help them avoid health problems such as fatal and non-fatal heart attacks and strokes and the need for bypass surgery or stent implantation. These health hazards are collectively referred to as 'a major vascular event' referred to herein as an *mve*. The pharmaceutical companies who manufacture statins and the health services who direct doctors to prescribe them believe the number of people taking them should be increased in order to provide more members of the public with protection from an *mve*. In contrast, many medical researchers and doctors argue that these drugs are being needlessly given to millions of people who are not ill but are deemed to be at significant risk of suffering an *mve* in the future. The critics say that the benefits of statins are being exaggerated and the risks associated with their use are being grossly understated. Arguments about the safety and efficacy of statins appear in the newspapers, on the internet and in public discussions. Even leading medical journals take issue with each other over the widespread use of these drugs to treat perfectly healthy people who do not have confirmed heart disease. Clearly this situation is not acceptable. The very thought that we may be harmed by drugs intended to improve our health prospects is a constant concern to many statin users and to many individuals who have been advised to take these drugs.

The arguments for and against the use of statins are complex. The pharmaceutical companies and the health service organisations which support their use say that the safety and efficacy of statins have been clearly demonstrated in numerous clinical trials carried out over the last 20 years. Their critics say that the evidence from these trials is not reliable and that in any event the claimed benefits do not justify the distribution of statins to a wide section of the population as very few of those treated actually receive that benefit. They further argue that a significant risk to health from side effects, both known and as yet unrecognised, is unacceptable when set against the tiny percentage of users who may benefit from use of the drugs.

The official analysis of clinical trials undertaken for and on behalf of the drug companies indicates that as few as one person in 100 treated for five years will benefit by delaying death from a heart attack for an unknown period and a further four in 100 will avoid or delay a non-fatal heart attack or stroke or surgical procedure over the same period. At the same time, they claim that common side effects such as muscle pain occur infrequently and are easily overcome by change of brand or dosage. Those who reject statin use claim that the small number of deaths are delayed for no more than a week or two after 5 years of treatment and that the extent to which other vascular events are delayed is unknown. More importantly they argue that side effects are more common and more serious than the statin providers admit and that there is a significant possibility of harm from long-term use of these drugs.

The uncertainty of the long-term outcome of statin use suggests that the authorities are gambling with the health of the public and it is therefore essential that this controversy should be resolved with the greatest urgency. Fortunately, there is a simple solution to the dispute which is staring the statin advocates in the face and it is the purpose of this booklet to ensure that the opportunity to end this controversy is taken up without delay.

Those who oppose the widespread use of statins argue that while the drug companies and health service organisations justify the treatment of a significant percentage of the population with statins relying on results derived from a limited series of clinical trials run between 1994 and 2011 and covering a total of around 105,000 statin takers, more than

7 million members of the public have effectively been participating in a trial in the real world by taking statins on a daily basis for up to 20 years. Rather than relying on predictions made from questionable results of old trials, would it not make more sense to find out what has actually happened to 10 or 20,000 members of the public who have been taking statins for at least ten years and comparing the impact of statins on their state of health and survival with a matched group of individuals who have not taken the drugs.

The information could be gathered from their medical records together with a visit to their GP for a physical examination, blood tests and completion of a questionnaire. The exercise could be completed in a few months by say 20,000 of our 60,000 GPs reviewing one statin-taker and a matched non-statin-taker. It would cost far less than a single clinical trial which lasts for two to six years and it would require no more than an hour or two of each patient's time. If serious health problems were encountered in any of the participants they could be referred for further investigation which would make it worthwhile for members of the public to attend. Pre-prepared cards with automated reading capability would minimise the time for analysis. The study would quickly reveal important information such as how many had died in each group, how many initially treated with statins had abandoned them and why, how many in each group had suffered health problems and whether specific problems were more common in one or other of the groups. In a matter of months, we would learn more about the effects of statins on the public than the clinical trials comprising the Lancet statin trial have provided in the previous 15 years of trials and 20 years of analysis.

In Part 1 of this booklet you will find evidence for and against the prescribing of statins. The claimed benefits of statins are easy to understand. Even if we ignore the criticisms and simply accept the questionable claims of the drug companies, the benefits are known to be minimal. The harm side however presents a more difficult issue. The number of side effects claimed by the statin advocates amounts to a little over one per cent of generally harmless and reversible muscle aches, with a trivial number of serious health conditions, whereas the number of side effects suffered by statin users identified by independent critics of the drugs is at least 17% with many users having serious long-term consequences. The most sinister threat is the possibility of premature ageing after long-term use due to reduced output of essential biochemicals which accompanies the unnecessary and probably harmful reduction in cholesterol levels.

In Part 2 of the booklet we look at the history of heart disease and review the several underlying causes of cardiovascular disease which have been identified by researchers over a period of many years. We show how the development of statins was based on the false premise that high levels of cholesterol are associated with the risk of heart disease and we identify the negative properties of statins which overshadow their minimal benefits which are now believed by many experts to be due to effects other than the reduction in cholesterol achieved by the drugs. If the independent retrospective assessment of the health of users and non-users called for in this publication shows that statin users are, on average, in better health than non-users after many years of use, the argument will be over and the public can accept without fear the expanded use of statins called for by the pharmaceutical companies, the NHS and other health service organisations such as NICE and the British Heart Foundation. If, however, the reverse is the case and a significant percentage of those taking statins have a high chance of being harmed, or exposed to premature ageing, their usage must be discontinued for all of those for whom the risks are significantly greater than the benefits, which may well be everyone. The pro-statin lobby should welcome the retrospective review called for in this publication as they have the most to gain. They will increase their sales if they are in the right and avoid the devastating consequences of continuing use of their products if they are wrong. Either way the public will benefit from the outcome of an appropriate review.

Finally, there is some heartening good news for the public in this booklet. While statins were conceived towards the end of a massive epidemic of severe heart attacks which raged between 1930 and peaked in 1970, that disaster, explained in Chapter 8, has been in continual decline for the past 47 years. British Heart Foundation statistics tell us that death from cardiovascular disease (CVD) fell by 74% between 1969 and 2013 for all ages and by 80% for those under 75. The decline started long before the invention of statins and it is still continuing on the same trajectory today.

Contents

PART 1

Chapter 1
The Statin Controversy

DETAILS OF THE DISPUTE BETWEEN THOSE WHO
SUPPORT THE USE OF STATINS AND THEIR CRITICS

If you are taking statins or if you are being advised to take them by your doctor, you may be aware that a serious controversy has arisen over the use of these drugs. You may, for example, have noticed headlines in newspapers which carry conflicting reports about the claimed efficacy and safety of statin treatment as a means of reducing your chance of having a fatal or non-fatal heart attack or stroke or of needing a surgical procedure such as a coronary bypass operation or a stent implantation to improve blood flow in the arteries of your heart. These events are collectively referred to as a major vascular event abbreviated herein to the term *mve*. More importantly, you will have seen widely divergent claims about the number and severity of side effects suffered by those who take statins. As an example of this controversy the *Daily Telegraph* newspaper of 1 August 2017 carried the headline 'Statins needlessly doled out to millions simply because of their age' while on the same day *The Times* carried the headline 'Give statins to almost all men over 60, GPs are told'. Nor is the argument confined to the newspapers. In September 2016 *The Lancet* medical journal published a meta-analysis which is referred to herein as the Lancet study.[1] It was overseen by the Clinical Trial Service Unit (CTSU) based in Oxford and claimed that statins save many individuals from *mves* and that around one in 100 users suffer from non-serious side effects which are quickly and easily dealt with. One week later the *British Medical Journal (BMJ)* carried an editorial suggesting that the Lancet study was far from realistic. In the editorial,[2] the Editor in Chief, Fiona Godlee stated:

> Independent third party scrutiny of the statins trial data remains an essential next step if this increasingly bitter and unproductive dispute is to be resolved. I have now written to England's Chief Medical Officer, Sally Davies, asking her to call for and fund an independent review of the evidence on statins.

However, over a year earlier, in June 2015, the Chief Medical Officer had already lodged her own request for 'an expert review to shore up public confidence about the safety and effectiveness of medicines, in the wake of controversy around statins and Tamiflu'.

In her letter to Sir John Tooke, President of the Academy of Medical Sciences, she wrote as follows:

> I am very concerned about the lack of resolution of the statins and side effects issues in both the medical and general press… there seems to be a view that doctors over-medicate, so it is difficult to trust them, and that clinical scientists are all beset by conflicts of interest from industry funding – and are therefore untrustworthy too. It cannot be in the interests of patients and the public's health for this debate to continue as it is.

In response to the CMO's request, in June 2017 the Academy of Medical Sciences issued a report on a study it had made of the controversies over the risks and benefits of common drugs. The report[3] included the following remarks:

The study found that just one-third of the public have confidence in evidence from medical research – compared with two-thirds who trust the experiences of their family and friends.

The pharmaceutical industry was particularly mistrusted.

Polling of more than 1,000 GPs found 82 per cent thought clinical trials funded by the sector were often biased to produce a positive outcome. That view was shared by 67 per cent of the public, in a poll of more than 2,000 adults.

In the USA where an estimated 35 million people are taking statins, Marcia Angell made the following observation in her book *The Truth about the Drug Companies, How They Deceive Us and What to Do About It*:[4]

It is simply no longer possible to believe much of the clinical research that is published, or to rely on the judgement of trusted physicians or authoritative medical guidelines. I take no pleasure in this conclusion, which I reached slowly and reluctantly over my two decades as editor of *The New England Journal of Medicine*.

How, we may ask, can such divergent views be held by those associated with these medical journals, all three of which are ranked in the top five medical publications in the world. And if three bodies of experts cannot agree on the safety and efficacy of statins, how are the general public to make up their minds whether or not to accept this treatment, which is given to millions of members of the public who are not ill, but who are judged to be at risk of becoming ill over the succeeding years of their lives? Surely, we are entitled to know with certainty what degree of benefit we will enjoy if we take these drugs and what degree of harm we may suffer from known, and possibly as yet unknown or unrecognised, adverse effects.

This whole issue is of immense importance for the future health of the nation. Already, in the UK, around 7 million people are taking or are, at least, supposed to be taking statins. The supporters of statin use say that this number should be dramatically increased in order to provide protection from a major vascular event to all who can benefit from statin therapy. They claim that a further 4 million adults in the UK would benefit[5] from the treatment saving an additional 200,000 individuals in the 'at risk group' from an *mve* or death over a period of five years. That suggests there would be around 40,000 fewer fatal and non-fatal heart attacks, strokes, bypasses and stent procedures per year out of an extra 4 million treated with statins. At the same time, it tells us that an additional 3,800,000 people taking statins would gain no benefit at all from the drugs, but they would nevertheless face the risk of adverse effects which, according to *The Lancet* study, would amount to some minor inconvenience for about 40,000 users over the whole five-year period.

On the other side of the dispute, numerous independent doctors and medical researchers argue that the reality is somewhat different. They say that the number of individuals saved from major cardiovascular events is much lower than that suggested by the statin lobby, that there is little evidence of how long the alleged postponement of the *mve* and particularly of death lasts and that taking statins can result in both short-term and long-term health problems. They also express the view that long-term use of statins to modify the biochemical processes of the human body, perfected over hundreds of millennia by evolution, could in the end result in a disaster of herculean proportions.

Both of these groups of medical specialists cannot be right and the object of this publication is to suggest how this controversy can be brought to an end in the interests of public health. Many experts argue that the independent scrutiny of the statins trial data called for in the *BMJ* editorial will do little to identify the risks and benefits of statins in use in the real world. This data has, after all, been derived from old trials carried out between six and 23 years ago, with each trial lasting from two to six years. They compare participants on statins with others on a placebo which looks like a statin but is a harmless inert substance. The number who received statins in these trials is a very small percentage (< 1.5%) of the 7 million individuals presently claimed to be taking statins in the UK.

It is therefore appropriate to call for a retrospective study of say 10,000 to 20,000 statin users, who have been taking statins for at least ten years, each to be compared with a non-statin user of the same age, who had similar characteristics (e.g. similar cholesterol levels, blood pressure and other relevant 'risk factors'), at the date when the statin user commenced taking statins.

The difference between this proposed retrospective study and the original prospective trials would be the emphasis placed on the overall health of the subjects. Doctors would look at any and all negative health aspects of both groups including an increase in deaths or disability from any conditions that may have been linked to statin use. This would include increased signs of premature ageing which has been strongly predicted for long-term statin users by some scientific experts. It would be up to the panel of experts controlling the study to make sure that all benefits and consequences of statin use were monitored in order to understand whether they had provided a net gain or loss in healthy living and life expectancy over the years of use.

To allow readers to make some judgements of their own it would seem reasonable to provide full details of both the positive and negative attributes of the drugs but as this publication is prompted by serious concerns relating to statin use and as comprehensive evidence of the claimed benefits of statin use is widely promoted by the pharmaceutical manufacturers and the health authorities, it is perhaps appropriate to concentrate in the main on the negative aspects of statin use. Nevertheless, the benefits and risks claimed for statin users by the pharmaceutical companies and the organs of healthcare are also set out in this publication.

Of course, any information contained in this publication cannot go unchallenged. Readers cannot be expected to make a judgement on the basis of the limited contents of this booklet but they may, after looking at the evidence provided, decide to lend support to the call for a comprehensive review of the levels of safety and efficacy of statins which have been achieved in the real world over many years of use.

I should add that the appeal for such an enquiry is not based simply on a personal opinion. The evidence against statin use contained in this publication has been generated by hundreds of doctors, medical researchers and scientists and I have simply taken the opportunity to assemble their industrious efforts to separate facts from fiction in pursuit of the health and safety of the public. Thus, when the pronoun 'we' is used in this booklet it represents the large number of doctors and scientists who hold the particular opinion being expressed.

If those who question the safety of statin drugs prove to be in the right, reducing or even halting the usage of these drugs will prove beneficial for millions of people who will avoid serious harms and the anticipated life-threatening condition of premature ageing in both the short and long term. If, however, the supporters of statin use have correctly predicted their safety and efficacy, a substantial number of additional users will be able to start taking statins with confidence that they will enjoy a net benefit from doing so.

This is a matter which can no longer be ignored by the statin manufacturers or the health authorities who support them. Only Members of Parliament are capable of instructing the necessary investigation of these potentially harmful drugs by a body that is not under the influence of either Big Pharma or the healthcare authorities, both of which have a huge financial interest in the continued widespread use of statins. In discussing this with doctors and other interested parties I have often been asked who should pay for such a review. I have answered firstly that the cost would be very low as the main labour component would be three or four hours of work from around one third of

the country's large number of GPs already paid for by the NHS. If, however, the cost of the study turned out to be significant, the obvious answer would be that the pharmaceutical companies should foot the bill. It is after all their products which are being brought into question and it is perfectly reasonable to ask companies who are wishing to increase the usage of their products to spend a tiny portion of their huge profits to prove beyond doubt that they are providing a net benefit for those treated with the drugs. Whatever transpires, the costs involved in a retrospective review would be trivial in relation to the weekly cost of statins to the NHS.

CHAPTER 2
The Two Sides in the Statin Wars

HUGE PROFITS FOR BIG PHARMA
AND THE PROMISE OF BIG SAVINGS FOR THE NHS,
BUT ARE STATINS GOOD FOR OUR HEALTH?

In the UK, the National Health Service has adopted the policy of treating members of the public with statin drugs as a means of reducing heart disease and strokes. These drugs are given to two distinct groups of people. They are given to people who have proven heart disease in what is classified as 'secondary prevention' and they are given to people who do not have proven heart disease but who are considered to be at high risk of having a major vascular event in the next five or ten years because they have 'risk factors' such as high blood pressure, high levels of LDL cholesterol and family history of heart disease. This is referred to as 'primary prevention'.

While many competent doctors and medical scientists have produced compelling evidence that statins are relatively ineffective and potentially harmful, these findings are simply ignored by the pharmaceutical companies who manufacture and sell the drugs and the healthcare authorities, such as the NHS, National Institute for Health and Care Excellence and the British Heart Foundation, who advise and instruct doctors to prescribe them. If there is even the smallest possibility that the drugs do suffer from serious deficiencies, how can these bodies continue to press for more and more widespread use of statins while refusing to investigate the claims of so many competent critics who have produced serious evidence of their limitations? The reason why Big Pharma and the healthcare authorities, who back their questionable claims, behave in this way are explained below. They can be summed up in a single word – MONEY.

THE STATIN LOBBY
Big Pharma

You will read in this booklet how Big Pharma have managed to turn a drug, which in the opinion of many experts should never have been approved by the regulatory authorities, into the biggest financial success they have ever enjoyed. For the pharmaceutical companies, profit is the driver and health is a secondary issue. They saw in statins the opportunity to produce what is in financial terms the perfect drug. It can be prescribed to a significant percentage of the public who are not ill but 'at risk', it does not provide a cure and users must take it for the rest of their lives to benefit from its alleged reduction in *mves* which, as previously stated, include fatal or non-fatal heart attacks or strokes, coronary bypass operations, or stent implantations.

In a way, statins are used like a vaccine and given to many people who are perfectly well on the basis that it will prevent them from becoming ill in the future. No one knows which persons among those 'at risk' will benefit and which of them will simply be exposed to any adverse effects of the drugs with no benefit at all. In these circumstances it is absolutely essential to ensure that the clinical trials which show the safety and efficacy of the drug are rigorously undertaken with the results known and accepted by all relevant experts as well as doctors and patients alike.

Instead of exercising the highest level of diligence in carrying out these trials, the drug companies have withheld raw data from which the trial results were derived so that independent experts cannot verify the conclusions drawn from the trials. In addition, the body which oversees the publication of the trial results – the Clinical Trial Service Unit (CTSU) – has admitted to receiving £268 million from the pharmaceutical companies over the past 20 years[6] which raises concerns about the extent to which their work is carried out under the influence of the drug companies.[7]

The influence of the pharmaceutical companies on both the research organisations which carry out work on their products and the regulatory organisations – such as the Food and Drug Administration in the USA and the Medicines & Healthcare products Regulatory Agency in the UK, which approve the drugs for use, is also of great concern. Employees of some major pharmaceutical companies can be found in the role of advisors to such agencies and there is evidence of significant influence being brought to bear in support of particular products or in favour of a particular scientific approach to a drug development.

In a remarkable publication issued by the FDA under the title 'Statins: A Success Story Involving FDA, Academia and Industry', the author, Suzanne White Junod PhD, who is credited with the role of FDA historian, explains how the FDA salvaged the statin project after Merck terminated clinical trials of the project. The following is a quote from the referenced paper:

> In 1959, FDA had approved the marketing of Triparanol as a cholesterol-lowering agent. In 1962, the drug was withdrawn from the market after FDA discovered that the company had provided falsified laboratory data. The falsified data had omitted reference to the cataracts found in rats and dogs in pre-clinical trials, and some patients who had taken the drug for a year did develop cataracts.
>
> When rumours surfaced that Compactin itself might have caused some cancers in dogs, Dr. Roy Vagelos, Merck's CEO, says that he 'made the decision to discontinue clinical trials of Lovastatin'. Following Merck's decision to terminate clinical trials, FDA became actively involved in maintaining interest in the development of the 'statins'.

This is the equivalent of the police receiving the confession of a failed arson attempt and urging the perpetrator to have another go. Surely if the pharmaceutical company is sufficiently concerned about the potential harmful effects of a drug to terminate clinical trials it is not for the regulatory agency to persuade them otherwise.

Big Pharma is also seen to influence academic institutions which undertake studies related to their products by providing funding for this work. It is extremely difficult, if not impossible, to find any studies exposing a deficiency of a drug product which have been funded by pharmaceutical companies while many positive and supportive studies receive significant amounts of funding. Even the placing of advertising by pharmaceutical companies in medical publications is seen in some cases as a means of exerting pressure for the inclusion of supportive studies in the publications in question.

As indicated earlier, the huge pharmaceutical companies are no longer trusted by a majority of doctors and members of the public and confidence in those who look after our health must be quickly and comprehensively restored.

The Healthcare Organisations: The National Health Service (NHS), the National Institute for Health and Care Excellence in medicine (NICE) and the British Heart Foundation (BHF).

While it is easy to understand how large commercial organisations can be blinded by the opportunity to earn huge profits, it is more difficult to comprehend how the organs of healthcare can be involved in placing members of the public at risk without proper investigation of the legitimate concerns of credible scientific experts. The main reason is once again a monetary one. The concept of prescribing statins to prevent individuals from suffering *mves* has been sold to the NHS on the basis of cost reduction. As we all know, the NHS is desperately short of funds and part of the reason for that is because large sections of the public have been designated as patients when they are, in fact, perfectly well and destined to live long and healthy lives. Nevertheless, it is attractive to the NHS to save many millions of pounds hospitalising and treating over extended periods of time, patients who have suffered heart attacks and strokes. While the desire to reduce costs of caring for heart disease patients may be commendable, it does not excuse a failure to properly investigate the claimed harmful effects of statins which could in the end incur costs to the NHS and to society far exceeding the savings derived from a relatively small reduction in non-fatal heart attacks and strokes.

The importance of money in this situation is evidenced from the fact that, in *The Lancet* study on which the justification for statin use is now largely based, the claimed cost-effectiveness is mentioned in the very first paragraph of this extensive technical document. It is clear that the mission of the CTSU is first and foremost to advance the claimed financial rather than the medical advantages of statins. The pharmaceutical companies have persuaded the NHS and other bodies that this is a win-win situation. They claim a significant reduction in the number of non-fatal heart attacks, strokes and procedures such as coronary bypasses and stent implantations using low cost statins which they tell us have only a small number of adverse effects on the huge number of individuals who take them, most of whom receive no benefit at all. Sadly, as we see below, even this monetary argument is flawed.

As heart disease deaths continue to decline due to causes other than the use of statins, the number of people who must be treated with statins in order to show a significant benefit is increasing dramatically and there is also the looming disaster of having to begin paying for the vast damage to the health to which statin use may lead. If this is not the case, it is up to Big Pharma and the NHS to show beyond any doubt that taking statins for the rest of one's life is a worthwhile exercise for the individual and society as a whole and does not simply postpone and/or increase infirmity in the latter portion of our existence.

A common argument for the use of statins is that statin treatment has resulted in a steady decrease in heart disease mortality in most countries. However, it is clear that the dramatic decline in deaths from heart disease began in 1970, long before statins were brought into use, and there is no evidence that the introduction of statins from around 2000 onwards has made any contribution to the rate of decline in heart disease. In contradiction to the claim that statins have had a visible beneficial effect since their introduction, major cardiovascular events in the USA actually increased for a few years following the introduction of statins. The American National Health and Nutrition Examination Survey (NHANES) found that during the period 1999–2006 the number of heart attacks and strokes in the US increased, the mean LDL cholesterol level decreased, and the self-reported use of lipid-lowering drugs increased.[8] Furthermore, statin utilisation in 12 European countries between 2000 and 2012 was neither associated with coronary heart disease (CHD) mortality nor with its rate of change over the years. In some countries statin use and heart mortality had increased while in other countries it had declined.[9] The long-standing decrease in cardiovascular mortality is most probably due to reducing consumption of trans fats, decreased sources of oxidation of cholesterol (such as smoking and drinking chlorinated water), improving control of infectious diseases and better treatment of acute heart conditions with increased use of bypass and stenting procedures.

The Critics of Statin Use

If one side of the statin dispute is represented by a coalition of Big Pharma and what I refer to as the healthcare services, then who represents the other side of the argument? It is not a single institution which can be simply identified, but rather a collection of diverse organisations and individuals who have set out their criticisms in a huge body of scientific papers, journals, books and, of course, internet articles and video presentations. One thing must be evident; there is no money in challenging the use of statins. No one is going to pay for proof that something doesn't work and may be harmful. In fact, the very reverse is the truth. Experts who question the reliability of the statin clinical trials or raise issues like acute muscle pain and weakness, diabetes, sexual impotency, cognitive decline and memory loss in statin users are reviled by the statin lobby. Those who question the safety and effectiveness of statins do so often at considerable risk to their careers, simply because they believe we are mistaken in our attempt to clumsily redesign the working of the human body.

If there is one group which has raised its head above the parapet in this dispute it is an organisation called THINCS, which stands for The International Network of Cholesterol Skeptics. THINCS recently published a book with the title *Fat and Cholesterol Don't Cause Heart Attacks and Statins are not the Solution.*[10] The book is edited by Paul J Rosch MA, MD, FACP who is Clinical Professor of Medicine and Psychiatry at New York Medical College and amongst other affiliations is a Fellow and Life Member of the American College of Physicians. He has also served as President of the New York State Society of Internal Medicine. On the back cover of the book is a dedication to Uffe Ravnskov MD, PhD, 'for his seminal achievements in disputing the dogma that fat and cholesterol cause coronary heart disease, and that statins are safe and cardio-protective for everyone'.

I have mentioned this book and these individuals to emphasise that critics of statins can be found in the highest echelons of medical science. I personally became interested in the subject of cardiovascular disease after reading Uffe Ravnskov's book *The Cholesterol Myths*[11] first published in English in 2000. From this I learned of the false premises upon which the development of statins was based and thereafter my eyes were fully opened by many further works generated by doctors and scientists throughout the world. In the following chapters I have summarised as best as I can the case against statins. I have tried to keep scientific language and terms to a minimum which I hope will make the information more accessible for the average reader.

For and Against

The case for statins is easily made. It is based on the outcomes of official clinical trials carried out over a period of years. Following analysis, the outcomes are presented in detailed reports published in various medical journals. The levels of safety and efficacy presented in these reports is widely publicised in the media by means of favourable articles and in advertisements showered on the public by the pharmaceutical companies. In addition, tens of thousands of drug company employees visit medical practitioners regularly to emphasise the benefits of their drugs and downplay adverse effects. A research paper published online by the USA Journal of General Internal Medicine[12] in 2007 included the following observations:

> Among the most prevalent conflicts of interest are those arising from physicians' interactions with drug company sales representatives, or 'detailers'. Pharmaceutical companies employ about 90,000 detailers (in the USA) and spend over $7 billion annually to market their products to physicians, averaging $15,000 per year per physician. Prescribing decisions can become conflicted by free gifts, meals, travel and other benefits. Because physician–detailer interactions bias medical decision-making, undermine public trust, and increase healthcare costs, the medical profession is now under unprecedented pressure to 'recognise, disclose to the general public, and deal with conflicts of interest'.

The same sales pressures are present in the UK. In addition, GPs have been offered a financial bonus for prescribing statins to those who qualify for their use. Recently, the healthcare authorities tried to extend the number of individuals who qualify for statin treatment from those at 20% risk of an *mve* over the following ten years to individuals with just a 10% risk which would have increased the numbers provided with statins by several million. They even sought to increase the financial incentive given to doctors for prescribing statins to all who 'qualified for treatment'. This initiative was quashed in the face of the objections by doctors to the change as reported in a February 2015 issue of the *Sunday Express* under the heading 'Medical experts furious that doctors will be paid to dole out "risky" statins' which continued as follows:

Doctors are set to get extra payments to hand out controversial statin drugs to patients who face a low risk of ever developing heart disease. It could mean four in 10 adults, including most of those in late middle age, are put on regular doses and a move that 'medicalises' healthy people leaving them at risk of side effects including diabetes and memory loss... Yet many heart specialists say that, for a large number of patients, benefits do not outweigh the risks which include diabetes, cataracts, debilitating muscle pains, memory loss and fatigue.

THE KEY ISSUES IN THE CASE AGAINST STATINS

The case against statins is a complex one. It extends into several different areas of concern which go beyond the challenges to the levels of safety and efficacy of the drugs claimed by the pharmaceutical companies and their supporters. The areas of concern are as follows:

- Serious doubts concerning both the safety and efficacy of the drugs in short-term and long-term use.
- Evidence that the underlying assumption, that a high level of cholesterol is the cause of arteriosclerosis and cardiovascular disease, is wrong.
- Evidence that the mechanism by means of which statins reduce the production of cholesterol interferes with the production of other critical biochemicals (isoprenoids) which is likely to result in short-term and long-term harm to users.
- Evidence that an equivalent or greater reduction in cardiovascular disease can be achieved by simple lifestyle changes without risk of long-term damage to health which is being ignored in relation to statins.

- Evidence that the heart disease epidemic which triggered the development of statins had entered into a continual decline before the invention of statins and that statins have made no contribution to this decline.
- Evidence that any success in delaying death or other *mves* is due to unforeseen effects of statins such as anti-inflammatory effects rather than reduction in circulating cholesterol.

CHAPTER 3
Claims and Counter-Claims

THE CLAIMS MADE FOR STATINS
AND THE EVIDENCE AGAINST THEM

In this chapter we are concerned with the claims made by the drug companies and endorsed by the organs of health provision such as the NHS, NICE and the BHF.

As most readers will be aware, a drug cannot be prescribed for use by the public unless it is approved by the regulatory agencies which are the Food and Drug Administration (FDA) in the USA, the Medicines and Healthcare products Regulatory Agency (MHRA) in the UK and the European Medicines Agency (EMA). It is generally agreed that the final step in approving a medicine for public use requires the carrying out of a randomised double blind placebo-controlled clinical trial in which the effect of a drug is measured against that of a placebo which is similar in appearance to the drug being tested but consists of a harmless inert substance. The term 'randomised' means that those taking the drug or the placebo are chosen on a random basis and the 'double blind' aspect means that neither the patients nor those involved in the trial know which patients are receiving the drug and which patients are receiving the placebo. These two measures are intended to ensure that there can be no bias in interpretation of the results.

Various different brands of statins have been subjected to clinical trials over a period of years beginning around 1985 with the last one included in *The Lancet* study starting in 2011. The individual trials lasted for between two and six years and the results of the trials were published as they became available. Although different trials were performed on different brands and had differing criteria and different end points, the results of a number of trials are sometimes combined into a meta-analysis which looks at common findings in order to obtain a more reliable understanding of the safety and efficacy of statin use. The interpretation of the results of the most recent such meta-analysis which combined the results of 27 individual trials covering a total of 175,000 participants was published in *The Lancet* medical journal in September 2016. It is referred to herein as the 'Lancet study'.

Because some of the trials were comparing different strengths of statins against each other rather than against a placebo, the total number of participants taking statins in the Lancet study was about 105,000 with about 67,000 participants on placebo. As mentioned earlier, there have been numerous criticisms of the Lancet study made by individual doctors, individual medical researchers and research establishments as well as the *British Medical Journal* editorial referred to earlier in this booklet.

The first point to emphasise in respect of the results claimed in the Lancet study is that the Cholesterol Trials Service Unit has denied independent researchers access to the raw data on which the analysis of outcomes has been carried out. When requests were made by independent third parties to view the raw data the CTSU stated that the pharmaceutical companies for which the trials were being carried out had refused to release the data. This of course raises the suspicion that the withheld data contains information which casts doubts over the accuracy of the results published by the CTSU in the Lancet study. In her previously mentioned editorial, Fiona Godlee, editor of the *BMJ*, concurred with the view that 'sharing the individual patient level data from the statins trials would send a strong message that no single person or group should have exclusive access to data that are so important for public health'.

An example of information withheld may be the details of a study with an 'active run in trial' where patients are given statins for a short period and any who show intolerance or severe side effects of a medicine at an early stage are not included in the trial. When this technique is used, it may explain the discrepancy in the reported number of individuals suffering side effects in the clinical trials when compared with findings of independent researchers who have followed the side effects encountered in daily use once the drug has reached the market.

On the following pages you will find the principal results of the Lancet study set out as a series of claims relating to safety and efficacy of statin use. These are divided into two sets of information covering both primary prevention (i.e. treatment of individuals with no heart disease but with high risk of future major cardiovascular events by virtue of their significant risk factors) and secondary prevention (i.e. treatment given to individuals with proven heart disease based on them having suffered a major cardiovascular event or by virtue of the results of clinical tests and measurements). In each case the specific claim made in the Lancet study is followed by a series of comments which present counterpoints to the claims, made by third parties, based on results of independent studies and reports issued by individuals or organisations which contradict the findings in the CTSU analysis. Each case carries a reference to the source of the contradictory findings listed at the back of the booklet, which can be viewed in detail on the net or in a specified publication.

In this booklet we are concerned mainly with the use of statins in primary prevention because it is in this form of treatment that many healthy people are exposed to the risk of adverse effects in exchange for a claimed minimal reduction in their risk of suffering a major vascular event. That is not to say that there are no concerns about the safety and efficacy of statins in secondary prevention. However, the risks and benefits of both primary and secondary prevention would be assessed in the independent retrospective clinical study that is proposed in this publication.

You will see from the following pages that the degree of variation between the Lancet study and the cited independent studies is very large. For example, it makes the difference between what would effectively be a degree of benefit in the delay of death, wherein perhaps one person in 100 treated in the primary prevention group and one person in 50 treated in the secondary prevention group would avoid a fatal heart attack or stroke (albeit for an unknown period of time), as compared with the findings from independent studies that no individuals would postpone death by more than a couple of weeks on average after five years treatment with statins.

Of even greater concern, however, are the findings in relation to adverse side effects in both treatment groups. The Lancet study suggests a number of side effects which are characterised as being non-serious and reversible, affecting around 1% of all persons treated, with only a very small number of serious or fatal side effects. This compares with a finding of a level of 17% and more of troubling side effects in both groups by independent studies with a very real possibility of severe side effects and potential widespread premature ageing after long-term use beyond say 10–15 years. This latter finding will be further explored in later chapters.

It has also been reported that the side effects suffered in general use cause a high percentage of users to abandon statins within a year or two of their adoption. In a particular Canadian study covering over 140,000 elderly people treated with statins, more than two-thirds had discontinued treatment after two years.[13] The most likely explanation is that they suffered various types of unacceptable side effects.

THE CLAIMS MADE FOR STATINS AS THEY ARE PRESENTED IN THE LANCET STUDY

Introduction
This review is intended to help clinicians, patients, and the public make informed decisions about statin therapy for the prevention of heart attacks and strokes.

As shown on the previous page, with respect to vascular deaths which comprise a fatal heart attack or stroke, in primary prevention (no proven heart disease but at risk), 1 person in 100 treated benefits by avoiding a fatal heart attack or stroke over five years of treatment and 99 out of 100 would not receive any benefit but would be exposed to any adverse effects as long as they continued to take statins and perhaps even after they stopped taking them. There is also no information on how much longer the additional survivor lives. However, even this tiny level of benefit is challenged by independent researchers who have reached different conclusions.

Here is what they found:

---

1. How much longer will you live if you take a statin? Doctor Malcolm Kendrick.[14]

Results:
Two studies were considered, both in secondary prevention (i.e. proven heart disease where the statin effect should be the greatest). In the HPS study, the average increase in survival time was 15.6 days and in the 4S study, the figure was 17 days, both after 5 years of treatment. On this basis, taking statins for 1 year would provide an average life extension in secondary prevention of 3 days.

2. The effect of statins on average survival in randomised trials, an analysis of end point postponement. Malene Lopez Kristensen, Palle Mark Christensen, Jesper Hallas.[15]

Results:
6 studies for primary prevention and 5 for secondary prevention with a follow-up between 2.0 and 6.1 years were identified. Death was postponed between 5 and 19 days in primary prevention trials and between 10 and 27 days in secondary prevention trials. The median postponement of death for primary and secondary prevention trials were 3.2 and 4.1 days, respectively after 5 years of treatment.

Conclusions: Statin treatment results in a surprisingly small average gain in overall survival within the trials' running time. For patients whose life expectancy is limited or who have adverse effects of treatment, withholding statin therapy should be considered.

---

3. Statins and all-cause mortality in high risk prevention trials involving 65,229 participants – a meta-analysis of 11 randomised controlled trials.
Ray KK, Seshasai SR, Erqou S, Sever P, Jukema JW, Ford I, Sattar N.[16]
Published by the NNT group.

Results:
Data were available on 65,229 participants followed for approximately 244,000 person-years, during which 2,793 deaths occurred. The use of statins in this high risk primary prevention setting was not associated with a statistically significant reduction in the risk of all-cause mortality.
Results updated November 2017

BENEFITS	HARMS
No statistically significant mortality benefit	1 in 21 experienced pain from muscle damage
1 in 217 avoided non-fatal heart attack [myocardial infarction] (preventing heart attack)	1 in 204 developed diabetes mellitus
1 in 313 were helped (avoided non-fatal stroke)	

Risks

Typically, treatment of 10,000 patients for five years with an effective regimen (e.g. Atorvastatin 40 mg daily) would cause about five cases of myopathy, one of which might progress, if the statin therapy is not stopped, to the more severe condition of rhabdomyolysis, 50–100 new cases of diabetes, and 5–10 haemorrhagic strokes. However, any adverse impact of these side effects on major vascular events has already been taken into account in the estimates of the absolute benefits.

Statin therapy may cause symptomatic adverse events (e.g. muscle pain or weakness) in up to about 50–100 patients (i.e. 0·5%–1·0% absolute harm) per 10,000 treated for five years. However, placebo-controlled randomised trials have shown definitively that almost all of the symptomatic adverse events that are attributed to statin therapy in routine practice are not actually caused by it (i.e. they represent misattribution).

COMMENTS:

Risks

The greatest disagreement between the statin promoters and their critics lies in the area of so-called side effects. The Lancet study results show tiny numbers of adverse effects which are typically myopathy (muscle pain and degeneration) which is argued to be reversible, an increased chance of becoming diabetic and a tiny increase in haemorrhagic strokes (haemorrhagic – bleeding as opposed to ischaemic – clotting strokes.)

As earlier stated, this controversy gave rise to an editorial in the *British Medical Journal* (*BMJ*), questioning the independence of the analysis presented in the Lancet study and demanding that the Chief Medical Officer of the UK should initiate an independent review of the statin data used in the study.

According to the Lancet study, adverse effects from statin treatment are extremely rare, they are generally reversible and their number can only be obtained from randomised controlled trials. However, many drug-related adverse effects in various therapy areas have emerged from observational studies and post-marketing surveillance.

In conflict with the Lancet study there are many independent studies which suggest that the incidences and severity of side effects reported in the Lancet study is grossly understated. For example, in a survey carried out in March 2013 published in the *Annals of Internal Medicine*, researchers tracked more than 100,000 statin users for nine years. During the study, 17% of those treated reported side effects.[17]

Yet another concern arises from the fact that the dosage provided by the different statins, although they work through the same mechanism, may have different strengths independent of dosage. In a later chapter we show how an early statin drug Baycol (Cerivastatin) manufactured by Bayer was recalled in 2001 after a series of statin deaths from kidney failure following rhabdomyolysis (death of muscle fibres, debris from which blocks the kidneys). Bayer boasted that Baycol was the most potent statin on the market and the Lancet report is providing results from the average strength of all the statins in the 27 trials included in the meta-trials. We therefore need to know the results for each different statin to see if some pose a higher risk than others. This information would be revealed by the proposed retrospective study.

Other researchers have identified serious side effects dismissed in the study as being non-existent or of little consequence. For example, a book authored by Duane Graveline, an astronaut who is also a family doctor, identifies previously unmentioned episodes of transient global amnesia, a condition in which subjects suffer from total memory loss for a period of between 15 minutes and 12 hours. Although this condition is unlikely to be reported by sufferers for a variety of reasons, he found that the FDA in the USA has recorded 30,000 cases over the past ten years.[18] This author has written a second book: *The Statin Damage Crisis*.[19]

In a review authored by independent researchers,[20] the authors have documented that statin treatment may result in cancer. Many statin experiments on animals have resulted in cancer and at least five human statin trials have resulted in cancer in the treatment groups; in three of them with statistical significance. Furthermore, several studies have shown that patients suffering from various types of cancer have significantly more often been treated with statins compared with healthy control individuals.

Many studies have shown that diabetes is a side effect as well. In the Women's Health Initiative, for instance, more than 160,000 elderly women were followed for up to five years. At follow-up almost 10% among those on statin treatment had developed diabetes, but only 6.4% among the untreated.[21]

If statins truly 'saved' large numbers of lives, or perhaps as more precisely described postponed deaths for a significant period of time and postponed non-fatal heart attacks and the need for bypass or stent insertion procedures with no significant risk of adverse side effects, they would be worthwhile both as a cost-saver for the NHS and for the benefit of event-free survival of members of the public. If, on the other hand, the incidence of harmful side effects is significant, it would tilt the balance of the risk to benefit ratio as the harms would quickly outnumber the benefits in matters of health and in relation to costs.

That is why the accurate assessment of the number and seriousness of side effects is so important.

Once again we assert that the resolution of this problem and avoidance of its most serious consequences can only be found through a rigorous retrospective study of a significant number of long-term statin users in comparison with matched individuals who have not been treated with the drug.

Claim that future adverse effects are unlikely

The large-scale evidence available from randomised trials also indicates that it is unlikely that large absolute excesses in other serious adverse events still await discovery. Consequently, any further findings that emerge about the effects of statin therapy would not be expected to alter materially the balance of benefits and harms. It is, therefore, of concern that exaggerated claims about side-effect rates with statin therapy may be responsible for its under-use among individuals at increased risk of cardiovascular events. For, whereas the rare cases of myopathy and any muscle-related symptoms that are attributed to statin therapy generally resolve rapidly when treatment is stopped, the heart attacks or strokes that may occur if statin therapy is stopped unnecessarily can be devastating.

COMMENTS:

Perhaps the most complacent and dangerous statement in the Lancet study is that concerning the predicted absence of future adverse effects. Chapter 9 of this booklet covers the sequence of events which has led to the use of statins, including the Nobel Prize-winning development of the drugs themselves. As will be seen, a vast body of evidence suggests that statins are an inappropriate treatment for cardiovascular disease by virtue of the fact that they function by reducing the creation of essential biochemicals in the human body and thereby compromise the essential process of cell energy generation and cell division upon which a healthy longevity depends. Many specialists believe that in long-term use over ten to 20 years or more, cellular depletion will lead to premature ageing. This condition has not so far been noticed because it has not been looked for and indeed an army of medical representatives constantly advise doctors that many conditions, which may be a consequence of the prolonged use of statins, have nothing whatsoever to do with statin treatment. That may be true but it is too easy to classify such problems as failing memory and cognitive decline as simply a consequence of growing older. We need proof that it is not a side effect of statins use which can be gained by comparison of those taking long-term statin treatment with others of comparable age and characteristics who have not used the drug. The key issue here is not how many trials have been done but how long they have lasted. In truth, I would rather we discover that statins are safe and effective as the drug companies and the organs of healthcare would have us believe, but what if they are wrong? What if we are exchanging some modest delay in major cardiovascular events experienced by a few for a progressive decline in health and fitness for many? What if the one person in 100 treated who was lucky enough to have avoided or postponed a major cardiovascular event is offset by dozens who suffer a reduced quality of life in what has been referred to as their golden years?

The previous chapters cover the basic arguments supporting the call for an independent review of the safety and efficacy of statins experienced by millions of users on a day to day basis. They can be summarised as follows:

- The evidence of safety and efficacy advanced by and on behalf of the pharmaceutical industry and the healthcare authorities is neither adequate nor credible. It is derived from outdated and questionable clinical trials and is thought to exaggerate the benefits of statins while at the same time grossly understating the risk of short-term and long-term harms resulting from their use.

- Even if the benefits are accurately determined, in primary prevention at least, they do not justify the treatment of large numbers of members of the public who may be put at significant risk of harm for a small reduction in their already small risk of having a major vascular event.
- No significant information is available relating to the length of time for which specific events are postponed and this is an essential body of information necessary for the accurate cost savings which are the justification of statin use for primary prevention accepted by the health authorities.
- A study of the underlying principles on which statin treatment is based suggests that statins do not work by lowering cholesterol but rather by an as yet undetermined 'pleiotropic effect' which could be related to an anti-inflammatory action or an effect which is analogous with correction of vitamin D deficiency.[22] Whatever the true cause of action may be, it produces an unacceptably small rate of reduction of vascular events in the very large numbers needed to treat (NNTs).
- A misleading conclusion from results of statin therapy arises from the finding in clinical trials that a higher dosage of statins produces a greater reduction in cholesterol and that this confirms the interpretation that cholesterol lowering is the mechanism by means of which vascular deaths and other *mves* are delayed. In fact the relationship between statin dose and cholesterol lowering merely shows that the reduction in cholesterol is dose-related and that higher dosage of statins increases whatever pleiotropic effect (e.g. reducing inflammation or increase of vitamin D

effect) actually causes delays in deaths and *mves*. It does not prove that cholesterol lowering is the mechanism which causes the claimed reduction in *mves*.

- Reviews of the mechanism of action of statins expose the destruction of cells by reduction in the availability of a number of isoprenoids which are essential for cell energy and cell division (mitosis). *See figure on page 76.* The likely outcome of long-term destruction of cells is premature ageing and there are already some indications that this is taking place in both short-term and long-term users. This poses a threat to the general health and longevity of users in old age.

- An understanding of the underlying causes of heart disease suggests that easily adopted lifestyle changes will achieve a greater reduction in vascular events. Research into such possibilities has not been pursued due to the exaggerated claims made for statins.

- Means of non-invasive determination of the presence and degree of atherosclerosis now make it possible to directly measure the effect of statins and compare it with the effects of harmless lifestyle changes. In addition, this development has the capability of limiting statin treatment to those with a measured high level of vascular disease (atherosclerosis) and by repeat measurements a year or more apart it would quickly establish whether treatment with statins (or any other treatment means) actually had an effect on the level of atherosclerosis in the individual.

- Clinical trials are conducted in order to predict the safety and efficacy of a drug intended for use in human beings. If trials are properly conducted and the evidence for the successful use of the drug is overwhelming, few, if any, doctors or research scientists will find reason to oppose their use and any negative findings from ongoing use reported by doctors using the yellow card system will be quickly investigated in order to decide whether there is any threat of serious harm to users. That is not what has happened in relation to statins. First of all, hundreds of doctors and scientists have challenged the fundamental justification for use of the drugs (i.e. cholesterol lowering) and pointed to damage inflicted on members of the public by versions of the drug similar to those which have been approved for general use. Detailed information on the outcome of clinical trials has been withheld and high levels of debilitating side effects have been identified by independent researchers and dismissed by the leading spokespersons for the drug companies. Even the National Health Service officials who have accepted these drugs, largely on the basis of their potential cost savings, have refused to take seriously claims of harmful side effects although they are now beginning to accept that doctors are prescribing the drugs to only one-fifth of those who qualify to take them. Some researchers have shown that over 50% of users have abandoned these supposedly life-saving drugs after a few years of use.

CHAPTER 4

NNT – The Number Needed to Treat

HOW PHARMACEUTICAL COMPANIES AND HEALTH
AUTHORITIES JUSTIFY GIVING STATINS TO MILLIONS
OF INDIVIDUALS IN ORDER TO SAVE A TINY
PERCENTAGE FROM A MAJOR VASCULAR EVENT

As explained at the beginning of the booklet, the problem of statin use has been compounded by the concept of treating people who have never had a heart attack and do not have proven heart disease (known as primary prevention), as compared to treating people who have proven heart disease which is termed as secondary prevention. Both primary and secondary prevention involve a concept known as the number needed to treat (NNT). It is defined as the number of people who must be treated with a medicine in order to cure one treated individual from the disease which the medicine is intended to treat.

For instance, the NNT for antibiotics curing conjunctivitis within 10 days is about 12: A dozen people with that eye infection need to take the drugs for one person who would otherwise remain infected to become cured. The other 11 either would have recovered on their own or they are not helped by the drugs. For statins one published NNT for delay in having a heart attack is 104. That means that you have to treat 104 people for a period of five years in order to delay one fatal heart attack or stroke for an unknown period. It's a similar result to that published in the Lancet study where we saw that with respect to deaths delayed they were claiming less than 1 person per 100 treated for five years had their death delayed for an unknown period which three independent studies calculated to be no more than a week or two. Clearly the average period of postponement of death or an mve is of great importance as if this period is very short, it would be pointless to take statins for the rest of one's life in order to gain the predicted benefit of taking the drug. So, what can we hope for? How much longer will you live if you take statins or how much long on average will it be before you suffer from a major vascular event? Neither the drug companies nor the NHS are able to give us any idea of the likely period of relief or extra survival. If you Google this very question on the internet you will be directed to three different sites already referred to in this booklet on pages 26 and 27. They will each tell you that one statin user out of 100 may on average live a couple of weeks longer than a non-user after five years of treatment. Out of 100 treated with statins 90 were not going to die anyway, 9 will die even though they were treated and one will survive for a week or two longer.

Why do you think the drug companies and the health care bodies including the NHS don't bother to tell statin takers how much longer they can expect to live? Is it because they don't know, is it because they don't think it's of any importance or is it because they are embarrassed by the miniscule improvement in their prospects if someone takes these drugs for the rest of their life. It could, of course, be because they believe that if the public were aware of these facts, they would stop taking statins which is, as we see elsewhere, precisely what is happening. The possibility of losing customers due to disappointment with the benefits of statins is certainly in the minds of the statin supporters. In the Lancet report which claims in its the first paragraph that it has been produced in order to inform the public about the risks and benefits of statins, we are told as follows:

It is, therefore, of concern that exaggerated claims about side-effect rates with statin therapy may be responsible for its under-use among individuals at increased risk of cardiovascular events. For, whereas the rare cases of myopathy and any muscle-related symptoms that are attributed to statin therapy generally resolve rapidly when treatment is stopped, the heart attacks or strokes that may occur if statin therapy is stopped unnecessarily can be devastating.

There is another important factor which will increase even further the number of people being treated with statins in order to achieve a given reduction in deaths and mves in the future. It is the decline in heart disease and strokes which began in 1970 long before statins came into use and which has continued to the present day. The table below shows the annual death rate from vascular deaths (i.e. from heart attack and stroke) per 100,000 population of men and women under the age of 75 over a number of different years. As can be seen, between 1995 and 2015 the death rate has fallen by a factor of 70% for men and 63% for women. Therefore, if a trial was started today we could expect the death rate in the placebo arm to be about one-third of the average death rate in the placebo arm found in the Lancet study which was 1.5% per year or 7.5% over five years.

Similarly, the deaths in the statin treated arm would be approximately one-third of the 1995 number and it would thus be necessary to treat three times as many patients with statins to delay a single death or major vascular event. Perhaps this is the reason why we are repeatedly shown results which were gathered between 12 and 23 years ago and why no attempt is made to update the clinical trials with ongoing examinations of those treated with statins.

Benefits	CORONARY HEART DISEASE DEATH UNDER 75		STROKE UNDER 75	
YEAR	Men	Women	Men	Women
1970	1,262	865	95	74
1980	521	174	72	54
1990	393	145	50	37
1995	308	112	40	30
2000	226	78	33	25
2005	155	71	24	19
2010	115	50	17	13
2015	96	42	12	8

Deaths per 100,000 population under the age of 75 from vascular disease for selected years between 1995 and 2015[24]

In October 2017, one day's headline in *The Times* and *The Telegraph* (and similarly in other newspapers) read as follows:

The Times: 'Doctors give statins to only one-fifth of patients who qualify'
The Telegraph: 'Doctors putting patients off statins'

One wonders whether we should be horrified or delighted by this news, but can it really be serious? As we are frequently told that 7 million people are taking statins in the UK, the reluctance to prescribe statins can only be a recent development and it would be interesting to know why such a dramatic reduction in statin usage is occurring amongst new statin users. Surely it can only be because the word has got around that side effects are more troublesome than they are claimed to be by the authorities. The statin lobby claims that this is due to false claims of adverse effects by uninformed opponents of statin use and 'imagined' or misattributed adverse effects. A more plausible explanation is that the adverse effects are more common and more troublesome than they are claimed to be. The true level of the nature and number of adverse effects would be quickly exposed by a retrospective review of patients. The above-mentioned newspaper report alone, recording that only one-fifth of qualifying members of the public are accepting statin treatment, justifies an immediate retrospective enquiry into statin use.

You can read more about this in a short booklet with the encouraging title 'YOU WILL NOT DIE FROM A HEART ATTACK'.[58] The author, Dr David Grimes, frequently posts interesting information on the relationship between cholesterol and heart disease as well as other medical issues. In this brief publication he gives a thorough account of the 20th century epidemic of heart disease. He points out that the epidemic spread in many countries that did not have access to trans fats which are now accepted by the health authorities in the USA and UK as the primary cause of the epidemic. One possible cause of the heart disease epidemic which he favours is an undiscovered bacterial disease. However, as both microbial action and trans fats have been shown to be a cause s of sudden blockage of coronary arteries leading to violent heart attacks known as myocardial infarctions so it may well be that the 20th century epidemic described in the Grimes booklet had a dual cause. The two graphs in David Grimes booklet showing the rise and fall of deaths in the UK between 1930 and 2010 and the comparative fall in the UK and France are reproduced below on the following page:

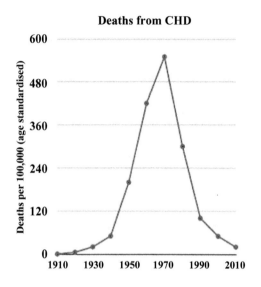

Deaths from CHD

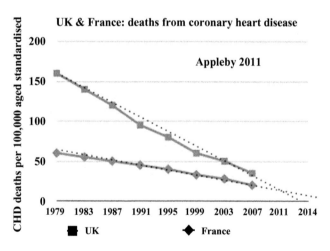

UK & France: deaths from coronary heart disease

Appleby 2011

The above discussion is concerned with the issue of efficacy of statin drugs, how effective they are and what benefits can we expect from using them but there is another equally important area of concern, which is that which bears on their safety. Is there any chance that they will cause us harm and if so, is it possible that the harm may exceed the benefits which they are claimed to provide?

Even the disappointing result recorded above in relation to efficacy may be acceptable to members of the public if there are absolutely no adverse side effects of statins, which are referred to as harms. The statin producers and health care providers tell us that harms caused by statins are minimal. We have seen that the all-embracing Lancet study claim only a tiny number of trivial adverse effects on the health of users but it is equally clear that many doctors and medical scientists throughout the world disagree with their findings. Is there an independent body which can act as a referee between the two sides in this argument? Fortunately, the answer is yes. The NNT group which specialises in publishing NNT results for all kinds of drugs is also concerned in another parameter of drug use which is the NNH. It stands for the Number Needed to Harm. This organisation looks at a wide range of trials carried out by official bodies and independent researchers and publishes a number which represents the number of individuals who must be treated in order to encounter specific harms from using the drug. This is a somewhat complex exercise because it covers only those harms which w frequently found and recorded in trials. The results are shown in pane 3 on page 27. Clearly 1 in 10 treated suffering muscle damage and 1 in 50 developing diabetes is a high price to pay for no difference in death and 1 in 60 postponing a heart attack for an unknown period. That of course is just a prediction from many official and independent clinical trials, often contradicting each other. We really do need to find out what has really been happening to statin users over the past 20 years rather than continuing the argument between believers and non-believers.

PART 2

Introduction

The foregoing chapters have dealt with the facts of the statin controversy with an analysis of the risks and benefits of statin use garnered from the authorities and from the works of independent doctors and scientists over many years. This alone does not answer the question of why statins are unlikely to be safe and effective or how and why they were developed and approved for human use in the face of serious criticisms of their validity over an extended period of time. In order to support the call for an independent retrospective study of statin use in the community, it is not necessary to understand the history of heart disease or the background to the development of the statins but for those readers who are interested, information on these subjects is provided in subsequent chapters. It does not require a high degree of scientific education to understand the motives and actions of all those involved. The development of statins was clearly driven by incentives other than a desire for the health of the public. Hopefully, along with many medical scientists and doctors, you will see the need to resolve this matter by means of the review called for in this publication before millions more are placed in harm's way, either by failure to accept this medicine or because of it.

CHAPTER 5
Early Research Into the Causes of Heart Disease

AMERICANS, KLOTZ AND MANNING, FIND AN
ASSOCIATION WITH INFECTIOUS DISEASES
AND RUSSIANS WITH RABBITS START THE
CHOLESTEROL MYTH

Even though deaths from heart disease at the beginning of the last century only accounted for about 10% of all deaths, it wasn't long before curious researchers began to try and understand what caused the disease. They knew from post-mortems that in older people who died of the disease there were fatty deposits in the walls of the arteries supplying the heart with blood. They were keen to understand where these deposits came from. In 1910 two American researchers, Oskar Klotz and M.F. Manning, performed autopsies to examine the arteries of young and old people who had died from a cause other than heart disease.[26] They found that the fatty deposits called atherosclerosis could be present in people of all ages and this suggested that heart disease often started in early life and usually progressed to become a fatal condition in later life. Below is a record of their findings from a series of experiments showing the ages at which the individuals had died and the incidence of fatty streaks in their arteries.

The most remarkable finding was the presence of incipient heart disease in younger people and the relative absence of the disease in older people (between 51 and 73) who had died from a cause other than heart disease. There was clearly a strong link between infectious disease and heart disease in subjects who had died of infectious diseases, while those who had avoided infectious diseases and lived to a good age had very little evidence of heart disease.

Age at death	Number of Cases Examined	Frequency of Fatty Streaks
1–10	16	4 Cases
11–20	12	8 Cases
21–30	15	12 Cases
31–40	22	7 Cases
41–50	15	4 Cases
51–73	10	1 Case

Table showing frequency of fatty streaks by age group

This suggests that infectious diseases had somehow accelerated the development of heart disease.

In their observations following their experiments, Klotz and Manning wrote:

In our experience these superficial fatty lesions were found most frequently in cases which had died of typhoid fever. In this disease it could be looked for with fair certainty in all individuals under 30 years of age. Frequently the condition was very marked, and it was only very infrequently that a considerable yellow streaking of the descending thoracic aorta was not found. In our records on typhoid fever in which the lesion was looked for at autopsy we have noted its absence in two cases only. This covers a series of 35 cases of typhoid fever.

The belief that infectious disease is a contributory factor in the development of atherosclerosis in the arteries has been proposed in numerous research papers and articles over the years and readers will be aware of recent encouragement to brush teeth to avoid gum infections and older cautions to take antibiotics when undergoing heart surgery. The question left hanging by the Klotz and Manning findings is quite how infectious disease can influence the development of atherosclerotic deposits in the arteries. An answer provided by Ravnskov and McCulley[27] explains how LDL cholesterol interacts with microbes leading to a series of events which end in the formation of a blood clot and subsequent blockage of the coronary artery.

A NEW APPROACH, RUSSIANS WITH RABBITS.

Within a couple of years of the Klotz and Manning research associating the progression of arterial plaques with ageing and also with the presence of infectious diseases, researchers in Russia were also looking to find the cause of the atherosclerosis but they already had a preconceived idea of where the deposits in the artery wall had come from. They were aware that lipoproteins which circulate in the blood contain particles of a substance which is found in the atherosclerotic plaque. They called this substance cholesterine, today we call it cholesterol.

This led them to undertake what may now be considered as a somewhat bizarre experiment. Led by Nikolai Anichkov,[28] a leading medical researcher, they fed rabbits with purified cholesterol obtained from egg yolks dissolved in sunflower oil. In 1913 Anichkov published a definitive paper reporting his findings from the rabbit experiments. The level of cholesterol circulating in the rabbits' blood quickly rose to four or five times the normal level and not surprisingly the rabbits began to develop fatty deposits in their coronary arteries similar to those found in humans with advanced atherosclerosis. The deposits in rabbits also appeared in other places in their bodies.

To many people that might seem to have been a pointless experiment. After all, rabbits eat grass not cholesterol and all the cholesterol in their bodies is manufactured in their cells from the grass they eat, the air they breathe and the water they drink.

Nevertheless, Anichkov was confident that it was the cholesterol circulating in the blood which ended up in the walls of the arteries. He continued his work with rabbits and ultimately satisfied himself that there was a clear relationship between the level of cholesterol circulating in the blood and the debris in the artery wall. One cannot disagree with his conclusion except to say that the deposition of cholesterol in the arteries did not occur unless the cholesterol circulating in the rabbits' blood was artificially increased to four or five times the normal level which could only occur in abnormal circumstances★ (*see* item at point 3 on page 50)

Anichkov concluded his 1913 report with the unwarranted

observation that the level of circulating cholesterol in the blood of human beings was a key factor in the development of atherosclerosis and therefore lowering the amount of circulating cholesterol would reduce the incidence of heart attacks. Without much thought, Anichkov and his followers translated an illogical experiment carried out on rabbits to the human domain in the firm belief that what happened in the grass-eating rabbits would be equally true for humans. This came to be known as the 'lipid hypothesis'. Later it would be the basis of a 'scientific' belief which sent many millions of individuals to an early grave.

Whether or not Anichkov's experiments were justifiable, the conclusions he drew from them were clearly flawed for the following reasons:

1. The experiments he carried out in grass-eating rabbits could not be reproduced in other animals such as dogs or rodents. All of these species, like humans, can ingest saturated fats and cholesterol without causing a significant change in the level of cholesterol circulating in their blood. In fact, only about 20% of the circulating cholesterol in man is obtained directly from food. The remaining 80% is synthesised in the cells of the body from biochemicals obtained from the breakdown of foods which do not contain cholesterol and apart from small and short-lived variations relating to the amount of fat consumed, the blood level of cholesterol remains fairly constant in a particular individual.

2. Anichkov admitted that he had fed relatively large amounts of pure cholesterol to the rabbits for an extended period of time and that their blood level was four or five times that found in a normal rabbit. Clearly the rabbits had abnormal cholesterol levels. The range of levels found in human beings varies from the mean level by about 50% plus or minus. Thus, a human being whose cholesterol level lies within the normal range cannot be said to have high cholesterol or low cholesterol. Over 99% of humans have cholesterol levels lying in this normal range.

3. ★A small number, (about one in 350 human beings), have abnormally high cholesterol which is known as familial hypercholesterolemia or hyperlipidaemia. This is now known to be caused by a faulty gene and it does predispose humans to atherosclerotic disease. In 1995 a Japanese researcher, Yoshinori Watanabe, found a species of rabbit with hypercholesterolemia with the same gene mutation found in humans with ultra-high levels of cholesterol. Nature had accidentally reproduced Anichkov's experiment by random gene mutation but not by feeding egg yolks to rabbits.

4. At least 50% of those who have heart attacks have what is now regarded as normal or even low cholesterol.

5. Clearly cholesterol was present in the arteries of the rabbits due to the excess levels in the rabbits' blood. It was not found in normal rabbits and therefore could not be said to be the cause of the atherosclerosis.

Quite apart from the imperfect logic of Anichkov's theory, the assertion that a significant percentage of human beings have unacceptably high cholesterol is preposterous. The elements of animal and human bodies have been fine-tuned by the evolutionary process over millions of years. If significant numbers had the disadvantage of having abnormally high cholesterol which sent them to an early death, evolution would have corrected that defect a long time ago. There is, in the view of many scientists, little doubt that the idea of competing with evolution to design an improved biochemical functioning of the human body by reducing the amount of cholesterol and, unintentionally, other key chemicals in an important biochemical pathway will lead to a disaster.

What happened to Anichkov's theory?

As Anichkov published his work mainly in Russia, there was little if any knowledge of his conclusions in the West for the next 40 years. It took an epidemic of a new and more aggressive form of heart disease to reawaken interest in Anichkov's theory. Details of this unfortunate development are set out in Chapter 8.

CHAPTER 6

Understanding Cholesterol

THE WAY CHOLESTEROL WORKS IN OUR BODIES
AND WHAT CONSTITUTES A NORMAL
CHOLESTEROL LEVEL

As the whole statin controversy revolves around cholesterol, it makes sense at this point for us to take a quick look at this much-maligned biochemical. This subject is somewhat technical but it is not too difficult to understand and worth the effort if you are interested in deciding whether it is advisable to take statins. In the future it will probably be taught to schoolchildren to make them aware of the importance of this precious substance and the way it can be damaged by certain avoidable activities.

Cholesterol is one of the most important substances in the human body. It is in every cell of the body and although the brain accounts for only 2–3% of body weight, 15% of all the cholesterol in the body is found in the brain. The total amount of cholesterol in people's blood varies from person to person but not by very much. You can see the range in the first graph on the following page. It's called a normal distribution or bell curve. As earlier stated, over 99% of the population are within the range and there is no reason to say that somebody has high or low cholesterol. The amount of cholesterol in your body is the right amount for you.

A second graph on the next page shows a finding from the Framingham study which has been one of the largest and longest studies carried out on the relationship between blood cholesterol, other risk factors and heart disease.[29] From this graph it is evident that although survival was more or less the same for all ranges of blood cholesterol, for the latter 30 years of the study shown on the graph, for men aged between 56 and 65, the highest level of survival was related to the highest cholesterol levels.

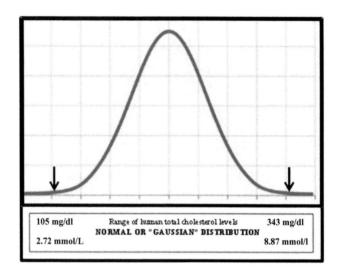

105 mg/dl	Range of human total cholesterol levels	343 mg/dl
	NORMAL OR "GAUSSIAN" DISTRIBUTION	
2.72 mmol/L		8.87 mmol/l

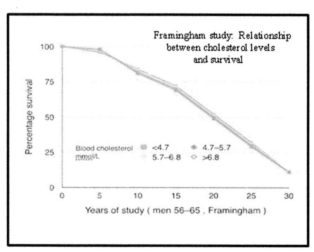

WHAT DOES CHOLESTEROL LOOK LIKE?

Pure cholesterol particles are not soluble in blood so cholesterol has to be carried round the body in a protein shell called a lipoprotein. There are several types of lipoprotein but the two types which are commonly referred to are HDL (high density lipoprotein) and LDL (low density lipoprotein).

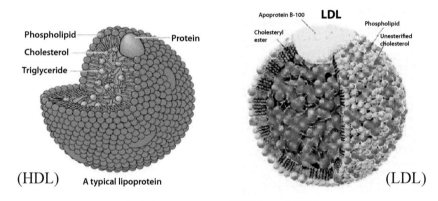

(HDL) A typical lipoprotein (LDL)

Artist's impression of HDL and LDL

Lipoproteins are composed of an outer water-soluble surface and an inner water-insoluble core. The HDL outer portion comprises phospholipid and protein with triglyceride and cholesterol particles forming the core. The LDL outer portion contains apoprotein phospholipid and un-esterified cholesterol. These two lipoproteins each have a different proportion of cholesterol and triglyceride. They are classified by density and the lower the density of the lipoprotein, the greater the amount of fats contained within it. Low density lipoproteins (LDLs) are cholesterol-rich particles. About 70% of plasma cholesterol occurs in this form. LDLs are chiefly involved in the transport of the cholesterol manufactured in the liver to various tissues of the body where it is used for a variety of purposes. Uptake of cholesterol into cells occurs when lipoprotein binds to LDL receptors on the cell surface. LDL is then taken into the cell and broken down into free cholesterol and amino acids. *The cholesterol in LDL and the HDL protein shells is the same — there is no such thing as good and bad cholesterol but cholesterol can be damaged by oxidation and as we will see later oxidised cholesterol participates in the formation of atherosclerotic deposits in the coronary arteries.*[30]

Both low density and high density lipoproteins have been in our bodies since the beginning of time. They are both essential for human and animal life and even for the survival of microbes. For years some scientists have been telling us that LDL is bad for us and that many people have too much LDL which causes cardiovascular disease. It is simply not true. People who have all levels of LDL cholesterol and total cholesterol, within the normal human range, which covers over 99 percent of the population, die from heart attacks in equal numbers. Indeed, if there is any direct association between the amount of cholesterol in our blood and heart disease it is the very reverse of what we are told. As we will see later, a number of studies have shown that higher levels of normal cholesterol have a tendency to be associated with living longer.

What then is the actual association of cholesterol with heart disease? It is that irrespective of the amount of cholesterol circulating in the blood, oxidised cholesterol is associated with a life-long progression of atherosclerosis in combination with the presence of damaged inner walls of arteries and other biochemicals in the human body. In normal circumstances this atherosclerotic process ends life in old age and it is probably the best way of dying. The fact that around 25% of all deaths result from cardiovascular disease which is often stated as an unwelcome fact by the health care authorities means that 75% of deaths are from other causes most of which are less acceptable than heart disease. However, a study of the mechanism of atherosclerosis formation provided later does open the door to some lifestyle changes which may contribute to both the reduction of premature deaths from cardiovascular disease (i.e. deaths under the age of 75) while at the same time achieving a limited increase in overall life expectancy.

CHAPTER 7

Cholesterol is Good for You

THE HIGHER THE LEVEL OF TOTAL CHOLESTEROL
IN YOUR BLOOD WITHIN THE NORMAL HUMAN
RANGE, THE LONGER YOU ARE LIKELY TO LIVE

Can that really be true? And if it is, why have we been led to believe that cholesterol is our enemy? The honest answer is because the notion that so-called high cholesterol is harmful has allowed commercial organisations to make billions in profits. The claim that high cholesterol in the bloodstream leads to heart disease has knowingly been used, first by the edible oil industry and subsequently by the pharmaceutical industry, to make untold fortunes.

You have read how it all started with a Russian rabbit experiment which, in the light of current knowledge, borders on the absurd, yet in the highest echelons of medical research the lipid heart hypothesis is still peddled as genuine science. Take a look below at a quote from the *Journal of Lipid Research*, the leading scientific journal which deals with the presence and role of fats in the human body. It was published in 2013 to celebrate the 100th anniversary of Anichkov's rabbit experiment and reads as follows:[34]

Nikolai N. Anichkov (1885–1964) first demonstrated the role of cholesterol in the development of atherosclerosis. His classic experiments in 1913 paved the way to our current understanding of the role of cholesterol in cardiovascular disease. Anichkov's research is often cited among the greatest discoveries of the 20th century. We at the Journal of Lipid Research take this occasion to acknowledge the debt we all owe to Anichkov and his colleagues for getting us on the right track.

In view of the hundreds of research papers written by experts over the past 20 years or more, it is simply inconceivable that the cream of lipid scientists are still offering praise to an individual whose misguided experiment led, and is still leading to, millions of premature deaths. Why are these scientists still pretending that Anichkov's views about the relationship between human cholesterol levels and atherosclerosis are remotely credible?

The answer has to be the influence of the edible oil industry now waning and Big Pharma, still waxing, both of which use their huge profits to persuade scientists into supporting the lipid hypothesis which was debunked years ago. If you are at the cutting edge of scientific research you will find it difficult to get funding for a project which proves high levels of cholesterol, which were allegedly caused by eating the wrong foods, are not the cause of heart disease. If you are an editor of a medical journal you will most likely find a considerable reduction in the support you receive from drug companies if you publish articles stating that cholesterol is good for you and should not be lowered with synthetic biochemicals. If you are a scientist working in the regulatory agencies such as the FDA in America or the MHRA in the UK you will not be able to keep your job if you tell your colleagues they are all wrong and cholesterol is not the enemy of mankind but its most important benefactor. Even your GP is offered a financial incentive to prescribe statins to 'lower your blood cholesterol', although, as earlier disclosed, doctors finally objected to the most recent attempt to influence them to prescribe statins to individuals with a lower level of risk of heart disease.

You will read later that another Russian researcher – David Kritchevsky – repeated the rabbit study in 1955. Since then numerous clinical studies around the world have shown that the incidence of heart disease is not related to the presence of so-called high levels of cholesterol in the bloodstream. Here are a few:

Krumholz HM et al. JAMA.272, 1335–40, 1994.[35]
Lack of association between cholesterol and coronary heart disease mortality and morbidity and all-cause mortality in persons older than 70 years.

CONCLUSION:
Our findings do not support the hypothesis that hypercholesterolemia or low HDL-C are important risk factors for all-cause mortality, coronary heart disease mortality, or hospitalisation for myocardial infarction or unstable angina in this cohort of persons older than 70 years.

RAMSDEN et al *BMJ*, 2016 Apr 12;353:i1246. doi: 10.1136/bmj. i1246.[36]

Re-evaluation of the traditional diet-heart hypothesis: analysis of recovered data from the Minnesota Coronary Experiment (1968–73).

CONCLUSION: Available evidence from randomised controlled trials shows that replacement of saturated fat with linoleic acid effectively lowers serum cholesterol but does not support the hypothesis that this translates to a lower risk of death from coronary heart disease or all causes.

Ravnskov et al *BMJ Open*[37]

Lack of an association or an inverse association between low density lipoprotein cholesterol and mortality in the elderly: a systematic review

CONCLUSION: Since the main goal of prevention of disease is prolongation of life, all-cause mortality is the most important outcome, and is also the most easily defined outcome and least subject to bias. The cholesterol hypothesis predicts that LDL-C will be associated with increased all-cause and CV mortality. Our review has shown either a lack of an association or an inverse association between LDL-C and both all-cause and CV mortality. In fact there was a 22% higher risk of death for each 30 mg/dL (0.78 mmol/L) **reduction** in serum cholesterol.

Behar S et al. Eur Heart J. 1997;18(1):52–9[38]

Low total cholesterol is associated with high total mortality in patients with coronary heart disease.

CONCLUSION:

Our findings clearly show that total cholesterol levels < 160 mg/dl were associated with an excess of non-cardiac and total mortality amongst 11,563 coronary patients of both genders aged between 45 and 74 years. The incidence of non-cardiac death was twice as high as in the control population, the most frequent single cause of non-cardiac death being cancer. It should be emphasised that these low levels of total cholesterol were pre-existing at the screening visit. They were not the consequence of pharmacological intervention.

Anderson KM, Castelli WP, Levy D[39]

Cholesterol and mortality. 30 years of follow-up from the Framingham study.

CONCLUSION:

After age 50 years there is no increased overall mortality with either high or low serum cholesterol levels.

The most recent and dramatic demonstration that so-called high cholesterol does not lead to heart disease and death was produced by Dr Zoe Harcombe, a PhD researcher, author, blogger and public speaker in the field of diet and health.[40] She took data from all of the (192) World Health Organization countries to produce four charts showing the relationship between average cholesterol levels and death rates from CVD and all causes per 100,000 population for men and women. Her results are shown below.

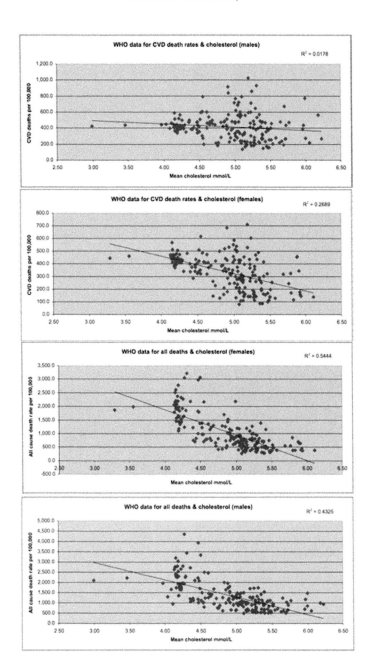

In each case the line drawn through the plots is called a Pearson product-moment correlation. If it slopes down from left to right, which it does, it indicates that a higher level of cholesterol has an association with lower death rates. Actually, you can see by just looking at the plots that the lower death rates tend to be associated with higher total cholesterol levels.

The tragedy is, that with the exception of Zoe Harcombe's charts shown above, all of the evidence showing that consumption of saturated fats and so called high levels of cholesterol circulating in the blood bear no relation to cardiovascular disease has been known to the authorities for many years. It was uncovered in the Framingham study mentioned above and generally suppressed by researchers because it did not agree with the prevailing myths which were being exploited by the edible oil industry. There is no better evidence of the deception which was being fed to the public of the time than the forthright statements subsequently made by two former directors of the Framingham study which are recorded below.

George V Mann MD
"Saturated fat and cholesterol in the diet are not the cause of coronary heart disease. That myth is the greatest 'scientific' deception of the century, and perhaps any century."
Professor of Biochemistry and Medicine
Dr. Mann was especially critical of the cholesterol-lowering trials. In this connection he is reported to have declared "Never in the history of science have so many costly experiments failed so consistently."

Dr William Castelli 1992
"In Framingham, Massachusetts, the more saturated fat one ate, the more cholesterol one ate, the more calories one ate, the lower people's serum cholesterol...we found that the people who ate the most cholesterol, ate the most saturated fat, ate the most calories weighed the least and were the most physically active." Dr William Castelli 1992 (Director of the Framingham study)

Chapter 8

Trans Fats – The First Stop on the Road to Statins

HOW THE EDIBLE OIL INDUSTRY LIED TO
THE PUBLIC ABOUT SATURATED FATS AND
CHOLESTEROL. IT LED TO THE PREMATURE DEATH
OF MILLIONS IN EUROPE AND AMERICA AND PAVED
THE WAY FOR STATINS

The astounding feature of the statin controversy is that it is an almost exact parallel of the last assault on society by a large industry which caused tens of millions of premature deaths often from a violent heart attack in the USA and Europe between 1930 and the present day. It was based on the same erroneous claims that high cholesterol is bad for us (the lipid hypothesis) and that eating fatty foods causes high cholesterol (the diet-heart hypothesis). It delivered vast profits to the edible oil industry, who conjured it up with the help of doctors, medical researchers, healthcare providers like the NHS and officials of government agencies. For 70 years, few members of the public knew that those who were claiming to be providing an ultra-healthy 'prudent' diet were poisoning them. In this tragedy many of us lost family members and friends, often at a young age. Here is a summary of the story as related in Wikipedia.

From about 1920 onwards a new kind of fat had been brought to the table by the edible oil industry. Margarine had been invented by

Hippolyte Mège-Mouriès in France in 1870 in response to a challenge by Emperor Napoleon III to create a butter substitute for the armed forces and lower classes. Margarine, like butter, consists of a water-in-fat emulsion, with tiny droplets of water dispersed uniformly throughout a fat phase in a stable crystalline form. The principal raw material in the original formulation of margarine was beef fat. Shortages in beef fat supply soon accelerated the use of improved methods of manufacturing fats and between 1900 and 1920 commercial oleomargarine was produced from a combination of animal fats and vegetable oils.

In 1901 Wilhelm Normann, a German chemist, invented what he called 'fat hardening', which was the process of producing saturated fats by pumping hydrogen through vegetable oils. During the years 1905 to 1910, Normann built a fat hardening facility in Germany. In 1908 the patent was bought by Joseph Crosfield & Sons Limited of Warrington, England and from the autumn of 1909 hardened fat was being successfully produced in a large-scale plant in Warrington. The initial year's production was nearly 3,300 tons. When Lever Brothers produced a rival process, Crosfield took them to court over patent infringement and lost.

The depression of the 1930s, followed by the rationing of World War II, led to a reduction in supply of animal fat and by 1945, 'original' margarine had almost completely disappeared from the market. It was rapidly being replaced by the synthetic form of fats produced by the hydrogenation of vegetable oils. In this process the addition of hydrogen to the unsaturated bonds in the oil results in saturated bonds, effectively increasing the melting point of the oil and thus 'hardening' it. It also results in a new form of fat called a trans fat. Trans fat has a similar composition to the saturated fats present in animal fats and dairy products but the molecule has a different shape which results in some problems when it is incorporated into cells in human tissues such as the wall of a blood vessel. Most animal fats – like butter, lard and tallow – have a large proportion of saturated fatty acids which have the correct molecular shape familiar to the human body.

Although it was initially unnoticed, the trans fats brought on an epidemic of a new kind of heart disease. Unlike the normal manifestation of heart disease which consists of progressive narrowing at certain points along the lumen or bore of the arteries of the heart, people began to die from a sudden massive heart attack called a myocardial infarction (MI). It happens when the internal wall of the artery covering the plaque within the artery wall ruptures causing a blood clot, sometimes mixed with debris from the plaque itself to enter the blood flowing in the artery.

The blood clot quickly causes a more severe blockage of the artery at the site of the rupture or in the first narrowing it reaches downstream. If total blockage occurs, depending on its location along the artery, it led to death within minutes. As the increase in heart attacks was following a previous progression, albeit at a more rapid rate, few noticed the change in the nature of some of the attacks and attention became focused on the treatment of heart attack survivors rather than gaining a better understanding of the cause.

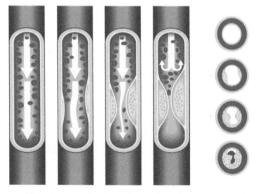

Showing progressive atherosclerosis   cross section

Showing myocardial infarction

cross section

Meanwhile, the epidemic grew in pace and deaths from heart attacks increased from 10% of all causes of death at the beginning of the century to a peak of 37% of all causes by 1970. By 1950, however, researchers were desperately trying to find an explanation for the build-up of plaque deposits in the artery wall and various theories were advanced from the possible association with infectious disease to the diet of fatty foods which people ate. Heart attacks were, after all, seen to be caused by what were classed as fatty deposits in the arteries known as atherosclerosis and people had always been eating a good deal of fat in their diets.

This view of the causation of the disease was given a boost in 1955 when another Russian researcher by the name of David Kritchevsky[41] repeated the almost forgotten rabbit experiments which had been performed by Anichkov in 1913. He again showed that the cholesterol found in egg yolks and animal fats was the same as the material clogging the arteries, *or at least he thought it was*. Actually scientists have since argued that the cholesterol in the arterial wall is oxidised cholesterol which was discussed earlier, but no matter – it was close enough to allow the blame for the blockages to be put on the cholesterol circulating in the bloodstream. So-called 'high levels' of circulating cholesterol now became the number one suspected cause of heart disease. But where had these new 'high levels' of cholesterol come from?

Two or three years after Kritchevsky's rabbit experiments, another player added fuel to the fire. His name was Ancel Keys. He was a professor in food physiology and one of his first contributions to this area of science was a paper in 1953, in which he stated that heart disease was caused by too much fat in the diet. In support of his theory he produced a chart showing the association between fat consumption and mortality from heart disease in six countries which he later extended to seven countries. The second study, known as the seven countries study, is the one most widely known.[42]

The study purported to show that there was a direct correlation between eating so-called saturated fats – found in meats, dairy products and egg yolks – and heart disease. It is now generally accepted that Keys had at his disposal data for fat consumption and heart disease deaths from 22 countries. He simply 'cherry-picked' the countries that supported his thesis that eating saturated fat caused heart disease. It is argued that if he had plotted the data of animal fat consumption against heart disease deaths for all 22 countries, his results would have shown that there was no relationship between fat intake and heart disease. The theory that consumption of foods containing saturated fats led to high levels of circulating cholesterol resulting in heart attacks and deaths came to be known as the diet-heart theory. It is different from the 'lipid hypothesis' which simply (wrongfully!) states that high levels of circulating cholesterol can lead to heart attacks and death. The difference is that the lipid hypothesis blamed 'high cholesterol' for heart disease wherever it came from, while the diet-heart hypothesis stated that the high cholesterol came from what we eat. Keys later accepted that there was no correlation between fat consumption and cholesterol levels.

At this point in time the edible oil industry, which was already enjoying mammoth profits from the increasing sales of their low cost trans fat – bearing solid fats and processed vegetable oils, which also contain trans fats, saw the opportunity to make an even greater fortune. Emboldened by the lipid hypothesis confirmed by Kritchevsky's repeat of the rabbit experiments and Keys' diet-heart theory, they launched an all-out campaign for the substitution of natural fats, which had nourished and sustained human beings for thousands of years, with trans fat products which produced defective cell membranes and structurally impaired tissues in the human body. These weaker membranes ruptured under critical pressure, clogging arteries already narrowed from what was seen as a natural ageing process with blood clots. By 1970, deaths from heart disease had reached a staggering 37% of death from all causes and untold numbers suffered from often fatal heart attacks at younger and younger ages, some dying before their parents. It must here be remembered that although average life expectancy was 71 in 1970, that average was produced by the combination of the many dying in their late seventies and eighties and even nineties being offset by the increasing number of deaths at 40, 50 and 60 years old.

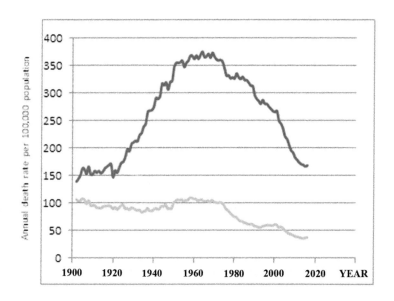

Graph showing the deaths from heart disease per 100,000 population in the USA from 1920 to 2015. The rate of growth of the disease in the UK and other European countries was similar. (Source[24])

Many scientists and doctors understood that the epidemic was being caused by the man-made fats themselves but they were overwhelmed by the propaganda of the edible oil and food processing industries who continued to champion the lipid hypothesis and the diet-heart theory. They used their ill-gotten wealth to corrupt scientists, government bodies and medical establishments. In the USA a government committee chaired by Senator George McGovern published a report which concluded, in addition to heart disease, that 'there is a strong correlation between dietary fat intake and the incidence of breast cancer and colon cancer' – two of the most common cancers in America. There were a number of studies that directly contradicted the McGovern Committee's conclusions. Greece, for example, had less than one-quarter the rate of breast cancer compared to Israel, but the same dietary fat intake. Spain had only one-third the breast cancer mortality of France and Italy, but the total dietary fat intake was slightly greater.

An American professor of comparative bioscience, Fred Kummerow, led the challenge against the edible oil industry's campaign to substitute synthetic fats for healthy saturated fats. He was joined in his struggle by a remarkable woman called Mary Enig and together they began to spread the understanding that the cause of the heart disease epidemic was not saturated fats and cholesterol but the artificial products which were being offered as substitutes.

Their story is well told in a publication by Mary Enig and Sally Fallon which appeared in *Nexus* magazine in 1998.[43] Some 20 pages long it provides a wonderful insight into what happens when an industry sees the opportunity to make a huge profit from a questionable product. It is being relived in the era of statins. I strongly urge you to take the time to read it.

'The Oiling of America' starts with a clarity of thought which seems to have eluded most of the characters who have occupied the history of heart disease enquiry. It began with a series of observations and a single question which read as follows:

> While turn-of-the-century mortality statistics are unreliable, they consistently indicate that heart disease caused no more than 10% of all deaths – considerably less than infectious diseases such as pneumonia and tuberculosis. By 1950, CHD was the leading cause of mortality in the United States responsible for more than 30% of all deaths. The greatest increase came under the rubric of myocardial infarction (MI) – a massive blood clot leading to the obstruction of a coronary artery and consequent death to the heart muscle. MI was almost non-existent in 1910 and caused no more than 3,000 deaths per year in 1930. By 1960, there were at least 500,000 MI deaths per year in the US. **What lifestyle changes had caused this increase?**

Unlike Kritchevsky and Keys, Enig and Kummerow did not assume that a significant change in the death rate from heart attacks was due to some inbuilt defect of humanity which had failed to show up until 30 years earlier. They assumed correctly that the epidemic was the result of some action of man which had changed dramatically in the previous 35 years. As food chemists, they suspected that it might be diet but they did not make the mistake of looking at food which had been around for thousands of years – they looked for something new and it didn't take them very long to find the trans fats.

Mary and her colleagues conducted a running battle with the edible oil industry and its executives who used every kind of ruse to discredit her. She published studies that showed how the heart disease epidemic paralleled the growth of synthetic fat sales. She published dozens of studies which showed that neither cholesterol nor saturated fats, both contained in healthy foods, were associated with deaths from heart disease. She publicised several large studies that indicated a link between consumption of high amounts of trans fats and coronary heart disease and possibly some other diseases, prompting a number of government health agencies across the world to recommend that the intake of trans fats be minimised. She showed that the statistics pointed to one obvious conclusion. It was not the traditional foods eaten in the early years of the 20th century which were causing the epidemic of heart disease. She argued that if Americans and Europeans had continued to eat traditional foods – including meat, eggs, butter and cheese – they would, like previous generations, have been kept healthy. In her view it was man-made vegetable oil-based foods that should have been abandoned.

Numerous reports had demonstrated over a period of time that the lipid hypothesis and the diet-heart theory were wrong. In particular the 1968 atherosclerosis project in which over 22,000 corpses in 14 nations were cut open and examined for plaques in the arteries showed the same degree of atheroma in all parts of the world – in populations that suffered from a great deal of heart disease and in populations that had very little or none at all. All of the published studies pointed to the fact that the thickening of the arterial walls is a slow, natural and unavoidable process. The lipid hypothesis was contradicted by the population studies and it did not in any event explain the tendency towards fatal blood clots that cause myocardial infarction.

In 1957 a project named the Anti-Coronary Club (ACC) was launched in the USA which selected businessmen from 40 to 59 to be placed on the so-called 'prudent diet'. The diet required the use of corn oil and margarine instead of butter, cold breakfast cereals instead of eggs, and chicken and fish instead of beef. The ACC members were to be compared with a matched group of the same age who ate eggs for breakfast and ate meat three times a day. It was believed that the 'prudent' diet would save lives. In 1966 the results of the ACC showed that the serum cholesterol of those on the prudent diet had dropped to an average of 220 compared to 250 in the control group but eight members of the ACC had died while all of the control group survived. The sponsors of the ACC study suggested that the study had an insufficient number of participants and a diet-heart study was proposed which would involve 1 million men. A pilot study involving 2,000 men resulted in exactly the same number of deaths in those on the prudent diet and those on the fat and cholesterol loaded control diet. In spite of the fact that advance preparations had been made involving substantial expenditures, the 'million man' study was abandoned 'for reason of costs'.

How did it all end?

In the UK it has not yet ended. Although there are regulations which require processed food supliers to detail the amount of transfats in their products few people understand the relationship between trans fats and heart disease. In the USA, after the premature death of a minimum of 20 million people over a period of 75 years, it is finally coming to a conclusion. In 2015 the United States Food and Drug Administration ruled that almost no trans fat could be added to food in America after a three-year grace period.

Steven Nissen, the chair of cardiovascular medicine at the Cleveland

Clinic said, **'In many ways, trans fat is a really tragic story for the American diet. In the 1950s and '60s, we mistakenly told Americans that butter and eggs were bad for them and pushed people to margarine, which is basically trans fat.'**[44]

But it was not a mistake. It was a deliberate perversion of the truth driven by corporate greed. No one was tried for these deaths or punished in any way. Most of those involved were dead long before the US Government recognised the tragedy. Some of those most responsible died from MI heart attacks caused by the trans fats they had vigorously promoted. How many people reading this have suffered the loss of a parent, grandparent or even a child from the consumption of trans fats.

Does all this seem familiar to you? A large wealthy industry influencing organs of the health agencies and government to tell the public that something is good for them when informed experts are showing it to be the reverse. Could that be precisely what is happening with statins?

This is how it was reported in two issues of *Time* magazine from 1960 and 2014:

Ancel Keys on the cover of *Time* Magazine in 1961. He claimed that saturated fats in the diet clogged arteries and caused heart disease.

Time Magazine cover story in 2014. Scientists were wrong about saturated fats. They don't cause heart disease after all.

Chapter 9

Statins Are Cellular Poisons

HOW BIG PHARMA USED THE LIPID HYPOTHESIS
AND THE DIET-HEART HYPOTHESIS AS AN EXCUSE
TO DEVELOP STATINS AND THE HORROR STORY
THAT SHOULD HAVE PREVENTED THE APPROVAL OF
STATINS

In the 1960s and 1970s, doctors and researchers were desperately trying to find a cure or at least a treatment for the massive growth in the number of heart attacks which had begun in the 1930s. Clearly the change of diet to synthetic fats was having no impact. Being the true cause of the problem, it actually made things worse accelerating heart disease deaths to 37% of all causes of death and at its peak in the early 1970s, killing 700,000 people a year in the USA and an equivalent number per capita in the UK.

It was not long before the large pharmaceutical companies became involved. They recognised that a drug which brought down deaths from cardiovascular disease would create huge revenues, particularly if it met their ideal criteria of being administered for the remaining lifetime of the user and being given as a protective measure to a significant portion of the population who could be said to be at risk of the disease by virtue of having certain risk factors, one of which was so-called 'high LDL cholesterol'.

The widely accepted lipid hypothesis, which had been propagated by the edible oil industry with cholesterol as the culprit, though challenged by many doctors and researchers, provided an attractive proposition to

Big Pharma and its researchers. It would be a simple exercise – reduce the body's ability to manufacture cholesterol. In this thought there was no hint of an attempt to verify the lipid hypothesis. Cholesterol lowering provided an agenda which could be followed without delay. The approach of the researchers can be observed in the online autobiography of Akira Endo,[45] a Japanese researcher who is seen as the father of statin research. He begins his journey towards statins with the following observations:

> While living in New York, I was very surprised by the large number of elderly and overweight people, and by the rather rich dietary habits of Americans compared to those of the Japanese. In the residential area of the Bronx where I lived, there were many elderly couples living by themselves and I often saw ambulances going to take an elderly person who had suffered a heart attack to the hospital. At that time, coronary heart disease was the main cause of death in the United States. The number of patients with hypercholesterolemia, a precursor to coronary heart disease, was said to exceed 10 million.

Endo had clearly made no attempt to understand the true causes of heart disease and had accepted that high cholesterol was the culprit. It must now be clear to readers that 10 million people could not be said to be suffering from hypercholesterolemia if the levels of cholesterol in their blood were within the normal human range and if half of those who died from heart attacks had blood levels of cholesterol which would be considered normal or even low by today's standards.

As mentioned in Chapter 6 there is a disease which occurs in families – hence called familial hypercholesterolemia – in which the levels of cholesterol in the blood reach levels similar to those found in the blood of Anichkov's rabbits after they had been fed with pure cholesterol for months. As previously discussed, this abnormally high level of circulating cholesterol is now known to be due to a defective gene present in about one in 350 human beings. Endo conveniently dropped the preface *familial* thereby demonstrating his ignorance of what constitutes hypercholesterolemia and thereby inventing a new disease in the general population. He further categorised the population who were carted off in ambulances as old and obese people when many of them would in fact have been in their 40s and 50s. None of this mattered to him. The agenda was set. Reduce the body's ability to make one of its most important chemicals with a new drug. In the rest of his autobiography Endo walks us through the science of statin development from toxic moulds which are available in thousands of different species. The purpose of the moulds in nature is to rot dead vegetable matter so as to recycle the environment and remove vast debris which occurs seasonally throughout nature. Even in his highly sanitised version of the history of statin development, we catch glimpses of disasters in which animals die of stomach cancer and suffer from many disease forms, including cataracts and muscle weakness, which are brushed aside by Endo like a bad day at the office. In truth, the history is evidence of systematic carnage of both animals and humans as Endo and other researchers ignore serious problems and doggedly pursue their goal to reduce the production of cholesterol in the human body with drugs – for no sensible reason other than profit.

The full story of the development of statins has been uncovered in a publication by James and Hannah Yoseph titled *How Statins Really Lower Cholesterol and Kill You One Cell at a Time*.[46] There is a 'made easy' version in which the title of the book is prefaced with the words 'Serial Killers'.[47] While these titles may seem to be inflammatory, anyone who reads these books will see that the use of the words is justified. They chart in detail the whole process of statin development starting from the point where statins were conceived and follow the actions and experiences of the research chemists and doctors involved. It can only be described as frightening.

A central issue in the book is the mechanism by means of which statins function in the body to reduce the output of cholesterol which is manufactured in individual cells, mainly in the liver but also in small amounts in all other cell varieties. The details are somewhat technical but they are not too difficult to understand, and if you are on statins you might wish to understand how they work.

All statins consist of a biochemical with the full name 3-hydroxy-3-methylglutaryl coenzyme-A reductase, although this is thankfully abbreviated to HMG CoA reductase and often to just reductase. This biochemical inhibits the production of certain biochemicals along a pathway in human cells known as the mevalonate pathway.[48] You can think of this pathway as a train line along which various biochemicals are manufactured and delivered for use in the cell. The figure on page 59 shows that cholesterol is at the end of the pathway and the very first 'pre-statin' to reach the market in 1959 called MER/29, or Triparanol, was produced by a USA company called Richardson Merrell. As you can see in the diagram on the next page, this biochemical blocked the mevalonate train at the tail just before cholesterol is delivered.

Triparanol was withdrawn from the market in 1962 after findings that laboratory employees had hidden or falsified reports of disastrous effects in animals such as cataracts in rats and dogs and muscle wasting in monkeys in pre-clinical (i.e. animal) trials.[49] Users who suffered a list of harmful effects, including cataracts and muscle wasting, issued civil suits against the company, most of which were settled out of court. Following this disaster, after a suitable pause, the statin development scientists turned their attention to 'reductase inhibitors' which, rather than interfering with cholesterol only, at the end of the chain, bring to a halt the production of biochemicals in the entire mevalonate pathway.[50] This is like throwing a hand grenade into the cell. It results in a reduced supply of each of the first five biochemicals in the pathway, all of which are essential to human life.

As shown in the mevalonate pathway illustration, these chemicals are involved in energy production in the cell and, more importantly, in aspects of the cell cycle which leads to cell division into two new cells (mitosis). If the cell does not divide when signalled it dies. If the cell dies, two daughter cells which should be produced are lost and any future cells that would result from further cell divisions are also lost. Over time this can result in effects such as weakening of the heart muscle or premature ageing which is difficult to differentiate from the normal ageing process.

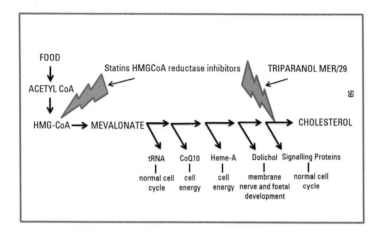

At this point in the statin development process some pharmaceutical companies began to recognise the risk of statin-associated cell damage and cell death. One company, Parke-Davis, withdrew from the field and wrote to the FDA about the risks of interfering with synthesis of biochemicals in the mevalonate pathway.[51]

Lipitor New Drug Application. (NDA)
Medical reviewer: Dr David G Orloff

Parke-Davis company to the FDA: 'Mevalonate is an intermediate, not only in the pathway to cholesterol but also in the synthesis of the prenyl, geranyl and farnesyl pyrophosphates (used in post-translational modifications of proteins), ubiquinones (compounds of the electric transport chain and critical in energy metabolism), dolichols (used in the maturation of glycoproteins), and isopentenyladenine (a compound of tRNA). **Cellular depletion of any or all of these metabolic products could be theoretically deleterious.**'

Similar actions followed in other companies. Because their statin known as Compactin (see ML-236B below) killed human cells in vitro, Beecham stopped statin development in 1976. After 1980 Sankyo followed suit and stopped ML-236B development after half of their laboratory dogs developed a rare cancer of the gut.

Another statin drug Baycol (Cerivastatin) by Bayer was recalled in 2001 after a series of statin deaths from kidney failure following rhabdomyolysis (death of muscle fibres, debris from which blocks the kidneys). Bayer boasted that Baycol was the most potent statin on the market. They never warned that it was therefore the most potent blocker of cell cycles. The more potent the statin the faster cell tissues and organs die. Fortunately, the problem was discovered early, otherwise a much larger number of people would have been harmed. Bayer paid $8 million in a multi-state settlement to plaintiffs. The statin research scientists were fully aware of the fact that all reductase inhibitors i.e. statins, had these devastating effects on the biochemicals in the mevalonate pathway. This is proven by the fact that Michael Brown, who with his colleague Joseph Goldstein won the Nobel Prize for 'discoveries concerning the regulation of cholesterol metabolism' filed a patent to counteract one effect of statins (reduction in production of CoQ10) which, as he knew, caused myopathy in animals and human beings. Myopathy is a muscular disease in which the muscle fibres fail to function resulting in muscular weakness and pain. If Brown, and presumably Goldstein, and Merck knew that statins caused myopathy, why did they not follow the Brown/Merck patent and add CoQ10, which is an essential source of energy for the muscle, to their statin. Was it because it would increase costs of testing and production of the double drug or because it would let everyone know about the consequences of interfering with the mevalonate pathway i.e. reducing production of CoQ10 which leads to myopathy and reduction of other essential isoprenoids?

Publication number: US 4933165 A	Coenzyme Q10 with HMG-CoA reductase inhibitors
US PATENT	US 4933165 A
Publication type: Grant	**ABSTRACT**
Application number: US 07/298,535	A pharmaceutical composition and method of <u>counteracting</u>
Publication date: Jun 12, 1990	<u>HMG-CoA reductase inhibitor-</u>
Filing date: Jan 18, 1989	<u>associated myopathy</u> is disclosed.
Priority date: Jan 18, 1989	The method comprises the
Fee status: Paid	adjunct administration of an
Inventors: Michael S. Brown	effective amount of a HMG-
Original Assignee: Merck & Co., Inc.	CoA reductase inhibitor and an effective amount of Coenzyme Q_{10}.

The patent was assigned to Merck proving their understanding of the risk of myopathy before their statin brand came onto the market.[52]

In his patent application, however, Brown did not mention a more serious consequence of blocking the production of CoQ10. Researchers at the University of Warwick and the University of California, San Diego have demonstrated that statins lower blood pressure. Clearly a heart which is deprived of energy will pump less efficiently and hence the blood will be propelled at a lower pressure. The drug companies have claimed statins lower blood pressures thereby resulting in fewer incidences of stroke and *mves*. Weakening the heart muscle with statins due to the CoQ10 blockade is probably a major cause of the decrease in blood pressure as well as the decreased risk of stroke and cardiovascular events, triggered by high blood pressure. Thus the mechanism of statins in reducing *mves* is partly at least achieved by making the heart less efficient.[53] As stated by another prominent critic, statins have not improved the net health of individuals. They have traded heart attacks and strokes for other serious illnesses. It may well turn out to be a one-sided exchange. One saved heart attack or delayed death for who knows which and how many other illnesses.

The fundamental flaw of statin science

This leads us to consider the fundamental flaw of statins. Although reported as a mere 'symptomatic' side effect occurring in up to 1% of statin users in the earlier mentioned Lancet study, the leading side effects of statin use, which is muscle pain from myopathy, is, according to one independent study, present in up to 17% or more of statin takers. It can clearly be seen that this 'side effect' is actually a predictable consequence of disrupting the mevalonate pathway. As stated earlier, other biochemicals which are removed from the mevalonate pathway are known to be involved in cell division and DNA replication. What are the consequences of eliminating these essential biochemicals in billions of cells? One unwelcome result is that the cell does not divide into two new cells when signalled to do so. It simply dies. Or it may mutate which could be even worse. In the course of researching the subject it is possible to find hundreds or even thousands of documents confirming the opinions and findings of expert medical scientists in relation to the dangers of statins. A good example of the enormous amount of analysis that goes into studies of the effect of statins on human biology is 'Statins and Myoglobin: How Muscle Pain and Weakness Progress to Heart, Lung and Kidney Failure' by Stephanie Seneff.[54]

That cell death is occurring due to statin use could easily be confirmed by reviewing a significant number of individuals who have been using statins for ten years or more and comparing them with people of the same age and characteristics who have not been on statins.

It is our belief that neither the pharmaceutical companies nor any public body has made any serious effort to investigate this critical concern. It is absolutely essential to determine if people are being harmed, suffering premature ageing and even dying from use of statins. Even the lowest level of cumulative damage to the human body does not justify taking drugs that are intended to lower cholesterol which is unnecessary and which many researchers have shown to be a harmful process in itself. Statins should never have been approved. The risks of using them have been understated and the benefits have been overstated. There is little evidence that statins 'save lives' or, as more correctly expressed, postpone deaths. There is growing evidence that statins cause harm.

As mentioned above, the first approved statin (Triparanol) was withdrawn from the market after it was discovered by chance that employees had hidden or falsified reports of disastrous effects in animals. The very fact that such adverse effects had occurred in both animals and, as subsequently found, in human beings, should have been enough to cause the FDA to call a halt to work in this field. It was suggested in a record of the litigation that the Triparanol disaster was proof that the lipid hypothesis was wrong and that again should have ended the search for cholesterol lowering drugs of any kind. [55]

Not only did that fail to happen, after a suitable pause other companies with their eyes on the promise of future billions in profit chose to enter the game with even more dangerous statins that would reduce the production of other critical substances created in the mevalonate pathway. Of course dramatic failures continued to occur in animal trials but no doubt these were either not communicated to the FDA or they were persuaded to ignore them by corrupted influential advisers linked to the drug companies as reported in the book Serial Killers. [46, 47]

Since all of the statins are extracted from toxic moulds and can therefore be classified as mycotoxins, and as they all act by the same mechanism of blocking the mevalonate pathway at the start, it is difficult to understand why the regulatory authority allowed work on these drugs to continue in a number of companies and as described earlier even encouraged the continued research and clinical trials of these drugs when the drug companies themselves began to doubt the wisdom of pursuing statin development. One credible explanation is that certain leading scientists in the field who were working on behalf of the pharmaceutical companies were also advisers to the FDA and held positions with other influential bodies such as the National Institute of Health consensus panel, and the American Heart Association. There is no question that huge influence was used by senior scientists on behalf of pharmaceutical companies to press on with the development of these dangerous drugs. We must also ask, what is the difference between each of the statins? They are all cellular poisons acting at the same point in the mevalonate pathway and the only difference that could be relevant is the strength of the statin provided by the different manufacturers. The higher the dose, the quicker the action in destroying the isoprenoids which are the key biochemicals produced in the mevalonate pathway.

The package inserts which are contained in every pack of all the different brands of statins read like a scientific textbook. They are required by law to inform the user of any negative consequences of taking the drugs but I doubt whether one person in a thousand would have any chance of understanding the language. Here is a general example in which I have substituted the word statin drug X for the named brand of statin:

> Statin drug X is a selective, competitive inhibitor of HMG-CoA reductase, the rate-limiting enzyme that converts 3-hydroxy-3-methylglutaryl-coenzyme A to mevalonate, a precursor of sterols, including cholesterol. It lowers plasma cholesterol and lipoprotein levels by inhibiting HMG-CoA reductase and cholesterol synthesis in the liver and by increasing the number of hepatic LDL receptors on the cell surface for enhanced uptake and catabolism of LDL.

The insert identifies cholesterol as one of the 'sterols' that is reduced but does not mention any of the other biochemicals in the mevalonate pathway which are reduced at the same time such as CoQ10 which is referred to in the above-mentioned Brown patent as follows:

'Folkers et al. states that these data show decreasing tissue levels of CoQ10 with increasing severity of the symptoms of cardiac disease.'

Can this statement be anything other than an admission that statins actually increase heart disease?

As stated above the package insert is intended to warn users of any dangerous consequences of taking the particular drug product but considering the abstruse language and omission of the specific risk of reduced heart energy, one can only assume that it is there to protect the pharmaceutical companies and all those involved in the delivery of statins to the public from claims that they failed to warn users about potentially dangerous side effects of the drugs.

In case there is any doubt left about the toxicity of statins, there is one more piece of information to take into account. The deadly effect of six statins on four common types of human cells: smooth muscle cells, fibroblasts, endothelial cells and myoblasts. All cell types stopped replicating in the presence of all six FDA-approved statins (as at 2013) in the following order of increasing potency (and therefore increasing risk of injury):[56]

Pravastatin
Lovastatin
Simvastatin
Atorvastatin
Fluvastatin
Cerivastatin (Baycol removed from the market in 2001).

Clearly the above condensed history of statin development demonstrates that there are serious concerns about the effects of statins on the human body and the millions of individuals who are taking these drugs are entitled to know what impact, if any, the long-term use of these drugs will have on their health. If there is to be a trade-off between a limited postponement of major cardiovascular events for five users in 100 (or perhaps it will now turn out to be five users in 200 or more) on the one hand and significant potential harms on the other we are entitled to know the exact odds and likely nature of each type of harmful event. An appendix to the earlier referred to publication 'Serial Killers' lists a total of 278 statin injury reports under the headings BIRTH DEFECTS, EYE INJURY, INTESTINAL INJURY, KIDNEY FAILURE, LIVER INJURY, MEMORY AND COGNITION LOSS, MENTAL ILLNESS (73), NERVE INJURY, PANCREATIC INJURY & DIABETES, SEXUAL DYSFUNCTION, SKIN INJURY, TENDON INJURY, THYROID INJURY AND OTHER INJURIES.[57]

This is not a horse race in which different tipsters can give us different estimates of risk and reward based on previous performance of the horses in races (clinical trials!) which took place between ten and 20 years ago. We need to know what has actually happened over the last ten to 20 years to a significant number of statin users and an equal number of matched individuals who did not take statins. Only a new and independent retrospective study can provide this information.

Chapter 10

What Are the True Causes
of Heart Disease?

AN EXPLANATION OF THE MECHANISM WHICH
RESULTS IN THE DEPOSITION OF ATHEROSCLEROTIC
PLAQUES IN CORONARY AND CAROTID ARTERIES
THROUGHOUT LIFE LEADING TO FATAL AND NON-
FATAL HEART ATTACKS USUALLY IN OLD AGE

As explained in a previous chapter, cardiovascular disease is a progressive
disease which is, in most cases, present throughout our lives. It is due to
a gradual build-up of atherosclerotic deposits in the arteries of the heart
until the interruption of blood supply to the heart muscle itself usually
results first in heart pain (angina) and shortness of breath and ultimately
in a heart attack. The accumulation of plaque in the arteries over many
years seems to be inevitable and by the age of 40 about half of us have
atherosclerotic deposits in our arteries. The best we can hope for is to
delay the progression of atherosclerosis for as long as possible and hope
that the final consequence is short-lived. A sudden heart attack in old
age is, for most, the best way to die. If we could eliminate heart disease
we would die of something else in old age, probably after a long period
of infirmity and with a poor quality of life. The major objective of heart
disease research should therefore be the slowing of the progression of
heart disease in younger people who could continue with an active life
for many years. It is a fact that in some individuals, additional factors

accelerate the progression of the disease to the point where death or a severe heart attack occurs at an early age and our efforts to treat heart disease should concentrate on identifying and treating these individuals. That does not require us to medicate half the population over 50, most of whom are not going to suffer a heart attack or death before they have reached the age of 75, 80 or older. The most fervent supporters of statin treatment admit that they may delay death from a heart attack or stroke for a short time in only a tiny percentage of those taking these drugs. To put things in perspective, in a high-risk group 7.5 people out of 100 might be expected to die within five years and the Lancet study claims that in the trials, statins reduced this to only 6.6 people dying in the same period so statins have delayed a fatal heart attack in less than one person out of 100 treated for five years and we don't know how much later that lucky person died. As reported earlier, independent analysis by three groups of experts suggested the average difference in longevity was no more than a week or two after five years of treatment.

The challenge therefore is to understand how atherosclerosis causes an early death in a relatively small number of people and find a way of identifying and treating those younger people who are more likely to die at an early age. In order to pursue this objective, we must develop an understanding of precisely how arterial plaques are created and why the process of plaque creation is sometimes accelerated in younger people. To start with we do know that the early deaths are generally caused by a myocardial infarction which is the blockage of an artery due to the formation of a blood clot when the plaque in the artery ruptures, allowing the clot and some of the plaque material to enter the bloodstream. It should be noted however that cholesterol-based substances (eg oxidised cholesterol or cholesterol esters) which are found in atherosclerotic plaques do not enter blood vessel walls in a uniform distribution throughout our bodies. Nor are they found at all in the veins. Clearly, therefore, some defects in the lining of artery walls must be present before cholesterol related substances can start to accumulate in particular locations in arteries. The current understanding of the progression of atherosclerosis through life is that it starts with damage to the surface of the internal wall of the coronary arteries at points where tortuous twists and turns are present in the arteries and particularly when blood pressure is high. In these locations epithelial cells are stripped from the inner surface of the vessels by the force of blood flow exposing the rougher underlying tissue. Certain biochemicals in the blood can also play a part in exposing the underlying surface. Oxidised cholesterol and other cholesterol related biochemicals attach themselves to the roughened areas probably as a kind of repair mechanism and blood clots also form over and around the new surface. This process can continue in a series of layers building an increasing thickness of plaque under the surface which eventually begins to bulge into the lumen (bore) of the artery creating a growing obstruction to blood flow.

As the blood flow is increasingly restricted symptoms of chest pain (angina) and shortness of breath start to occur. Finally a severe blood clot can completely block the artery causing a fatal or non-fatal heart attack. A larger blood clot can block the artery at an earlier stage causing a sudden heart attack known as a myocardial infarction often resulting in death within a few minutes with no previous warning symptoms. If this process can take a full lifetime to produce a fatal or non-fatal heart attack, why, we may ask, does it sometimes produce that result in a much younger person. There are a number of possible reasons for such an occurrence. For example, the damage to the arteries may have started early in life and may be more severe at an early age. Another possibility is that the individual's blood may be more prone to clot or the amount of oxidised cholesterol circulating in the blood may be greater resulting in a faster build up of plaque. All these variations depend on the blood chemistry of the individual which is in turn determined by the genes or other factors such as the concentration of oxidised cholesterol in the blood which can be increased by the ingestion or inhalation of oxidative substances. Another condition that appears to accelerate the development of atherosclerosis is the presence of infectious disease. As previously recorded two American researchers Klotz and Manning found that almost all young people who had died of typhoid had fatty streaks in their arteries indicative of incipient heart disease. Ravnskov and McCulley[27] suggest an interaction between microbes and oxidised cholesterol as a possible mechanism for the creation of vulnerable plaques which lead to myocardial infarction.

A good example of a substances which is known to attack the inner surface of the artery is a blood biochemical known as homocysteine. High levels of this substance in the blood are associated with a disease found in some children (homocysteine urea) which severely damages the arterial wall and can lead to atherosclerotic plaques in the coronary arteries of children as severe as those found in eighty-year-olds with advanced cardiovascular disease. Blood levels of another biochemical -cortisol- increase when a person is under stress and this is known to increase the likelihood of blood coagulation (clotting). High blood pressure which contributes to arterial damage is also known to be associated with heart disease. It is also an established fact that cholesterol, circulating in the blood encapsulated in LDL lipoprotein spheres, is more vulnerable to oxidation by several means including smoking[31] or consuming water containing high levels of chlorine which is added to the water supply to destroy infectious organisms. In his book Coronaries/cholesterol/chlorine published in 1969 Dr Joseph Price provides compelling evidence that chlorine added to drinking water accelerates the deposition of oxidised cholesterol in the arteries.[32] As discussed earlier the oxidised cholesterol adheres readily to the damaged surface of the blood vessels resulting in the generation of atherosclerotic plaque.

In a remarkable confirmation of the role of oxidised cholesterol in cardiovascular disease, a scientific paper reveals the presence of a cholesterol antibody in our blood.[23] Presumably its function is to return the modified cholesterol into a normal reactive state where it can be properly utilised in the human body. The answer to limiting the progression of atherosclerotic disease in our arteries is thus in the view of many scientists, not to interfere with the production of normal cholesterol in our bodies but to find ways to avoid and prevent damage to the inner arterial walls of our arteries and reduce, where possible, oxidative damage to our cholesterol.[33]

Chapter 11
A Healthier Life Without Statins

WHAT WE CAN DO TO IMPROVE THE HEART
HEALTH OF YOUNG AND OLD WITHOUT EXPOSING
OURSELVES TO THE SIDE EFFECTS OF POTENTIALLY
UNSAFE AND INEFFECTIVE DRUGS

Although we have established in this booklet that cardiovascular disease and stroke are the inevitable consequences of plaque accumulation over a lifetime there are some things we can do to reduce the impact of heart disease in the young together with some limited extension of life in the aged. That is what statins are supposed to do but we have argued that they fail to deliver any meaningful improvement in heart health and instead expose us to unacceptable levels of side effects and the unfortunate prospect of premature aging. Our hope is that this publication will lead to the establishment of a review of statin treatment which will show beyond doubt whether statins improve or damage our health. One thing that statins undoubtedly do is divert our attention from the possibility of simple treatments and lifestyle changes which may themselves achieve the improvements which statins have failed to deliver. In this chapter we review the explained causes of cardiovascular disease and suggest remedial actions for each of the causative factors which are either well established or supported by compelling evidence in published scientific literature.

The most promising opportunity to reduce heart attacks in the young arises from the development of a device which can measure the amount of atherosclerosis in the arteries non-invasively through a multifunction electrocardiogram.[25] This device is gaining a strong foothold in the USA, Japan and some other countries. Another device known as an impedance cardiograph is widely used for this purpose in India. If a simple non-invasive measurement can show how much atherosclerosis is present in the arteries, lifestyle changes which are believed to slow, halt or even reverse the progress of plaque deposition can be monitored through periodic measurements at yearly or greater intervals. This should quickly allow us to identify which of the suggested actions or lifestyle changes have the best effect in reducing or even reversing the progression of atherosclerosis and thereby keeping our hearts healthy.

Heart disease has been known to be associated with infectious disease since the studies of Klotz and Manning in 1911. The mechanism is thought to be an interaction between bacteria and cholesterol resulting in the formation of denatured or oxidised cholesterol which attaches to the damaged inner surface of the inner wall of arteries. Since tooth and gum infection is a common source of bacteria frequent brushing of teeth and use of antibacterial mouthwash may help to reduce incidences of infection. In addition, suspected infection should be promptly confirmed and treated with antibiotics rather than being allowed to develop in order to gain confirmation.

Inflammation is also understood to be associated with cardiovascular disease. The mechanism involved is thought to be an immune response to the development of plaque in the arteries which can lead to formation of blood clots and restriction of blood flow similar to that associated with ruptured arterial plaques. Reduction of inflammation is now thought by some researchers to be the mechanism by which statins achieve a small reduction in major vascular events rather than the claimed mechanism of cholesterol lowering. However, many anti-inflammatory drugs can be used to reduce inflammation without incurring the side effects associated with statin use.

It is also appropriate to mention here that a poor diet can result in health problems due to the consumption of unhealthy foods which may have low levels of necessary biochemicals and/or ingredients which are inimical to our metabolism. The important issue here is to follow advice from dieticians who have scientific knowledge of dietary requirements rather than relying on advertisements published by food manufacturing and processing companies which will often provide misleading information in order to increase their market share. A good example of such unhelpful information is the use of the term "vegetable oils" which although their description sounds healthy can in some cases contain trans fats introduced by deodorising and purification processes. A keen interest in diet pursued through properly qualified and reliable sources can make a real contribution to healthful living.

Regular exercise is also important. There are many scientific papers showing an association between lack of exercise and heart disease but once again expert guidance on what type of exercise is appropriate at different ages and how much exercise is necessary in order to maintain a healthy condition will prove helpful.

Other substances identified by Dr Malcolm Kendrick as vessel wall damaging agents or blood coagulating agents such as adrenaline and cortisol are secreted when a person is under stress. He argues that these agents are particularly harmful when eating food and that meals should be consumed in a relaxed state rather than in haste and when under pressure.[59] Dr Kendrick points out that the French generally take their meals in a relaxed fashion which may be responsible for their historically lower levels of heart disease as compared with the English. Some studies have shown the so-called Mediterranean diet to be effect in delaying heart attacks and death without any adverse effects, particularly in cases of proven heart disease.

For convenience of readers the remedial actions which are advocated to achieve a reduction in progression of atherosclerosis are summarised in the table below.

Disease Process	Protective and remedial actions
Damage to arterial wall	
By Homocysteine	Check level of homocysteine in blood. If above normal limit treat to reduce level with folic acid.
By high blood pressure	Treat with appropriate medication
By Cortisol or other stress related hormones	Practice relaxation particularly when eating.
Plaque deposition	Take measures to avoid oxidation of cholesterol. Avoid smoking and ingestion of chlorinated water by using filter
Infection as a precursor to plaque deposition	Brush teeth daily and use antibacterial mouthwash. Ensure prompt treatment of infection by undergoing infection check promptly upon suspicion of infection and treating infection without delay
Blood clotting tendency as indicator of thrombus formation.	Have blood clotting (coagulation) test to determine if treatment is necessary to achieve normal clotting tendency in order to avoid thrombus formation in arterial plaques
Inflammation with possible disruptive effect on arterial plaque	Check general level of inflammation and treat above normal levels with anti-inflammatory drugs
Extent of plaque burden	If available undergo periodic non-invasive measurement of plaque burden to determine if more intensive treatments are indicated.

As for the development of medicines to slow the progress of atherosclerosis, statins are supposed to do that but, as we have seen, there is little evidence that they succeed in reducing plaques and their side effects may turn out to be worse than the disease they are supposed to be curing. The pharmaceutical companies are in business to make a profit. They cannot be expected to look for food supplements or lifestyle remedies which will improve the health of our society without the need for costly – and sometimes dangerous – drugs. In the search for profit they are sometimes prepared to take decisions which are contrary to the interests of society. The agenda for what drugs we choose to develop and what costs and risks we are prepared to accept in treating a particular disease condition should be set by an organ of government which is not under the influence of the drug companies or healthcare providers, both of which are driven by financial considerations.

Clearly, a new mechanism for the financing of new drug development by governments, which end up paying for the drugs in any event, must be found. It would be a great idea to use such a financing method to get the drug companies working on new antibiotics, which our society is desperately in need of, but which are unlikely to be pursued because the cost of development would take many years to recover with little or no profit.

If the proposed retrospective study of statin use leads to the abandonment of statins it is clear that the vast revenues received by the pharmaceutical companies from sale of statins will diminish rapidly and as some portion of this income is used to support the development of new drugs it will be necessary to find a way of replacing it to ensure that research into new cures for major diseases continues. One way of resolving this problem would be to allow a small percentage increase in the pricing of all drugs across the board. In return governments should be able to direct research into drugs which are clearly needed by society rather than those which deliver the highest volume of sales and profit but do little to improve the health of the nation.

At the same time our medical scientists should be looking for the low-cost lifestyle changes which can reduce the impact of diseases. In this publication a number of promising approaches leading to a limitation of the progression of cardiovascular disease have been mentioned. A government department responsible for health policy as opposed to healthcare delivery could be set up to investigate potential remedies and lifestyle changes which could increase long-term survival as well as the quality of life enjoyed in our later years.

Summary

Following in the steps of the edible oil industry, the pharmaceutical companies have used unsubstantiated and discredited theories of the cause of cardiovascular disease to mislead the public into the belief that the level of LDL cholesterol circulating in the blood is harmful and should be lowered by treatment with statin drugs.

At the same-time they have created the false impression that we are in the middle of an epidemic of heart disease when in fact no such situation exists. Life expectancy at birth in the UK has steadily increased to an all-time high of around 83 for women and 79 for men, although in the last two years this progress has stalled, possibly due to the use of the very drugs which are supposed to be extending our lives and reducing both fatal and non-fatal heart attacks and strokes.

The drug companies, together with their allies in the healthcare services, claim absurd levels of efficacy of statins using statistical language such as 'relative risk reduction' which has led people to believe that they are at significant risk of dying or being incapacitated by cardiovascular disease when in fact the risk for all but the oldest members of the population (i.e. those older than 75) is remarkably low.

Whether or not statins can postpone death and major vascular events for a tiny percentage of those treated the authorities are unable to tell us for how long that postponement may last and more importantly they appear to have grossly underestimated the harms that may be suffered by 95% or more of those treated who receive no benefit in delay of death or mves. Even those few who avoid a major vascular event may find their health compromised by severe diseases in their later years.

The fact that statins act in the human body by interfering with normal biochemistry to reduce the production of numerous essential biochemicals associated with cell division, mitochondrial energy supply and other essential molecular processes provides an explanation for existing side effects. Evidence of these effects appears to be grossly understated as does evidence of serious long-term deleterious effects such as cognitive impairment, memory loss and premature ageing due to the loss of cell replacement through the process of mitosis (cell division).

In all of the history of medicine there has never been an attempt to modify the fundamental biochemical processes of the human body for a significant percentage of the population. Only vaccines are given on a widespread basis and they function by stimulating the immune system to produce antibodies to a given disease in a normal biological process.

An additional consideration is the belief among many researchers that simple lifestyle changes which can be easily evaluated will lead to a greater delay in the progression of atherosclerosis than that which is claimed for statins without any of the risks which are faced by 95% or more statin users who receive no benefit whatsoever from taking the drugs.

The debate over these issues cannot be ended by any amount of argument between opposing camps who simply disagree about the safety and efficacy of statin science. The matter can and must be resolved by a thorough review of the benefits enjoyed and harms suffered by a substantial number of long-term statin users in the real world as compared with the experiences of matched members of the public who have not been consuming the drugs.

As repeatedly stated in this publication, an independent retrospective study of the effects of statins will either vindicate the pharmaceutical companies and their supporters in the healthcare establishment, thereby supporting calls for the increased use of statins, or it will confirm the serious reservations of many doctors and scientists which will warrant the withdrawal of these drugs before large numbers of members of the public are harmed by their known and predicted adverse effects.

**PARLIAMENT MUST ACT TO DETERMINE WHETHER
THE RISKS WHICH ARISE FROM STATIN USE EXCEED
THE BENEFITS**

This booklet is associated with
The Statin Controversy website
WWW.THESTATINCONTROVERSY.COM

References

Full access to many of the references is limited to members of the publishing organisations or service.

1. Collins R and others. Interpretation of the evidence for the efficacy and safety of statin therapy. Lancet 2016;388:2532-2561. doi: 10.1016/S0140-6736(16)31357-5. http://www.thelancet.com/journals/lancet/article/PIIS0140-6736(16)31357-5/fulltext

2. Godlee F. Statins: We need an independent review. BMJ 2016;354:i4992 doi: 10.1136/bmj.

3. https://acmedsci.ac.uk/more/news/action-needed-to-preventconfusion-over-medicines

4. Angell M. The Truth about the Drug Companies: How They Deceive Us and What to Do about It. Random House, Neen York 2004 ISBN-13: 9780375760945.

5. https://www.theguardian.com/society/2017/aug/ 01/nearly-all-menover-60-and-women-over-75-eligible-for-statins-analysis-suggests

6. http://www.zoeharcombe.com/2014/08/ctsu-funding-from-drugcompanies/

7. Goldacre B. Bad Pharma: How Drug Companies Mislead Doctors and Harm Patients. Faber and Faber Inc. © 2013. ISBN-13: 9780865478008. https://www.scientificamerican.com/article/trial-sans-error-howpharma-funded-research-cherry-picks-positive-results/

8. Kuklina EV and others. Trends in high levels of low density lipoprotein cholesterol in the United States, 1999-2006. JAMA 2009;302:2104-10. doi: 0.1001/jama.2009.1672.

9. Vancheri F and others. Time trends in statin utilisation and coronary mortality in Western European countries. BMJ Open 2016;6:e010500. doi: 10.1136/bmjopen-2015-010500.

10. www.thincs.org

11. www.ravnskov.nu/CM

12. https://www.ncbi.nlm.nih.gov/pmc/articles/PMC1824740/ Physicians and Drug Representatives: Exploring the Dynamics of the Relationship.

13. Jackevicius CA and others. Adherence with statin therapy in elderly patients with and without acute coronary syndromes. https://www.ncbi.nlm.nih.gov/pubmed/12132976

14. https://drmalcolmkendrick.org/2015/10/27/how-much-longer-willyou-live-if-you-take-a-statin/

15. Kristensen ML and others. The effect of statins on average survival in randomised trials, an analysis of end point postponement. BMJ Open 2015;5:e007118. doi:10.1136/bmjopen-2014-007118. http://bmjopen.bmj.com/content/5/9/e007118.full

16. Ray KK and others. Statins and all-cause mortality in high-risk primary prevention: a meta-analysis of 11 randomised controlled trials involving 65,229 participants. http://www.thennt.com/nnt/statins-forheart-disease-prevention-without-prior-heart-disease /

17. http://annals.org/aim/article/1671708/ discontinuation-statins more than half stop one fifth symptoms

18. Graveline D. Lipitor, Thief of Memory. 2004. ISBN-13: 978-1424301621.

19. Graveline D. The Statin Damage Crisis. ISBN-13: 978-1424338696

20. Ravnskov U and others. The statin-low cholesterol-cancer conundrum. https://academic.oup.com/qjmed/article/105/4/383/1554800

21. https://www.ncbi.nlm.nih.gov/pubmed/25789118 Statin use and risk of diabetes mellitus.

22. Grimes D. Vitamin D and Cholesterol: The importance of the Sun. Publisher: Tennison Publishing ISBN: 978-0-9562132-0-4.

23. https://www.researchgate.net/publication/11969204 _Anticholesterol_ antibodies_ACHA_in_patients_with_different_ atherosclerotic_ vascular_diseases_and_healthy_individuals_ Characterization_of_ human_ACHA.

24. https://www.cdc.gov/nchs/data/dvs/lead1900-98.pdf Leading causes

of death 1900–1998.

25. https://www.premierheart.com/ webapp/contents/index.php

26. http://onlinelibrary.wiley.com/doi/10.1002/path.1700160117/abstract Klotz, O. and Manning, M. F. (1911), Fatty streaks in the intima of arteries. J. Pathol., 16: 211–220. doi:10.1002/path.1700160117.

27. http://www.ravnskov.nu/wp-content/uploads/2016/01/Am-J-MedSci-2012.pdf creation of vulnerable plaques by microbes in infectious diseases.

28. https://www.ncbi.nlm.nih.gov/pmc/articles/PMC1764970/ Anichkov.

29. Normal Disribution. https://www.mathsisfun.com/data/standardnormal-distribution.html

30. https://www.ncbi.nlm.nih.gov/pubmed/3560398 Framingham 30 years.

31. https://metabolichealing.com/good-bad-cholesterol-no-such-thing/

32. Coronaries/Cholesterol/Chlorine Reissue by Joseph M. Price (ISBN: 9780515094619) https://www.amazon.co.uk/Coronaries-CholesterolChlorine-Joseph-Price/.../0515094...

33. http://www.atherosclerosis-journal.com/article/S0021-9150(15)30095-2/abstract

34. https://www.ncbi.nlm.nih.gov/pubmed/23975896 anichkov anniversary.

35. https://www.ncbi.nlm.nih.gov/pubmed/?term=lack+of+association+between+cholesterol+Krumholz

36. http://www.bmj.com/content/353/bmj.i1246 Ramsden.

37. http://bmjopen.bmj.com/content/6/6/e010401 Ravnskov.

38. https://www.ncbi.nlm.nih.gov/pubmed/9049515 Behar Low cholesterol/mortality.

39. https://www.ncbi.nlm.nih.gov/pubmed/3560398 Anderson.

40. http://www.zoeharcombe.com/2010/11/cholesterol-heart-diseasethere-is-a-relationship-but-its-not-what-you-think/

41. http://ajplegacy.physiology.org/content/ajplegacy/178/1/30.full.pdf?ijkey=2ba2d7d125f06e3baf002a9af2879435883679d8&keytype2=tf_ipsecsha Kritchevsky.

42. http://www.zoeharcombe.com/2017/02/keys-six-countries-graph/
43. The Oiling of America http://whale.to/a/enig.html
44. http://edition.cnn.com/2015/06/16/health/fda-trans-fat/index.html
45. Birth of the Statins (I Akira Endo) (https://www.ncbi.nlm.nih.gov/pmc/articles/PMC3108295/
46. Yoseph H & J. How Statin drugs really lower cholesterol and kill you one cell at a time. ISBN-13 978-0-615-61817-3, Page 48.
47. Yoseph H & J. Serial Killers ISBN-13 978-0-9888206-3-0.
48. IBID 47 Page 7. Mevalonate pathway
49. IBID 46 Page 46. Triparanol MER/29
50. IBID 46 Page 47. Mevalonate pathway attacked at beginning
51. IBID 46 Page 74. Parke-Davis warns FDA
52. IBID 47 Page 63. Brown CoQ10 Patent
53. IBID 47 Page 66. Weakening of heart muscle causes lowering of blood pressure.
54. https://people.csail.mit.edu/seneff/statins_muscle_damage_heart_failure.html
55. MER/29 Story—An instance of succesful Mass DisasterLitigation http://scholarship.law.berkeley.edu/cgi/viewcontent.cgi?article=2831&context=californialawreview
56. IBID 47 Page 13. Statins kill cells in vitro in order of increasing potency
57. IBID 47 Page 207. Statin injury reports.
58. http://www.drdavidgrimes.com/ under ebooks.
59. www.thincs.org/Malcolm2.htm Essay by Malcolm Kendrick

ENJOYING
POETRY

ENJOYING POETRY

SADLER, HAYLLAR, POWELL

M

Macmillan Education

First published in 1981 by
THE MACMILLAN COMPANY OF AUSTRALIA PTY LTD

First published in this edition 1983

Published by
MACMILLAN EDUCATION LIMITED
Houndmills Basingstoke Hampshire RG21 2XS
and London
Associated companies throughout the world

Printed in Hong Kong

Illustrated by Julia Wakefield

Additional art by Julie Gross
Cover: Jim Lim

Contents

Contents

9. Writing Your First Poems

10. Rhythm

11. Strange Happenings

12. Alliteration

13. Poems to Compare

14. Personification

15. Feelings — **125**

16. Some Grave Poems — **137**

17. Birds of Feather — **139**

18. Ogden Nash — **147**

Contents

22. Machines **169**

Preface

A poem is not a delicate piece of pottery that
clumsy hands may drop and break in pieces. It
can be analysed, dissected, put under the
microscope; and the closer and more detailed
the examination, the more one finds to admire,
as with any work of art.

from *Feet on the Ground*
by Margaret J. O'Donnell

Poetry, like other fine arts, exists to be enjoyed and appreciated. The difficult task facing any teacher is that of developing this sense of appreciation and enjoyment in students who initially 'don't like poetry'.

Obviously, to some extent appreciation grows out of understanding. Students must learn to examine poems critically and thoughtfully, to see what the poet is driving at, to consider how well he or she is saying it, and so on. This does require work of some sort, but there is no other way to develop appreciation of poetry. The work can be at the talking level, with teachers and students discussing aspects of a poem and trying to refine their awareness of its impact on them by thoughtful analysis. It can also be at the writing level, with students attentively evaluating and communicating, in written form, the achievement and effect of a poem.

A sensitive teaching approach is needed — one that combines discussion and writing, one that examines ideas and feelings, one that encourages appreciation of the poetry of others while also giving room for the student to try his or her own hand at creating poetry — an approach that above all is built upon teacher-enthusiasm for poetry.

In this book, we have tried to offer raw material which we believe can be shaped into a poetry course aimed at developing an appreciation and an enjoyment of poetry. In particular, we have tried to present material that carries a high level of interest for students, while not neglecting the needs of quality. Furthermore, special units — on topics such as simile and metaphor, personification, alliteration, rhyme, rhythm, poetry-writing — appear throughout the book and provide a way of introducing students to the basics of poetry technique. In short, we believe that teachers will find this to be a poetry book that students can learn from and enjoy.

With poetry, as with many other pursuits in life, understanding brings enjoyment.

1. Similes and Metaphors

The poet works with words, often putting them together so skilfully that they call up pictures in our minds. Such patterns of picture-giving words are called **figures of speech**.

Two figures of speech that are commonly used to put us in the picture are the SIMILE and the METAPHOR. Let's take each in turn.

Similes

The simile asks us to picture one thing as being similar to another — often using the word 'like' or the words 'as ... as' to link our 'pictures' in the mind.

Examples:

She swims   like a   fish.   He's as hairy   as a   gorilla.

Get the picture? Good. Now try this exercise:

Similes are pictured below and overleaf. Supply the missing words.

The cook was as _____ as a _____

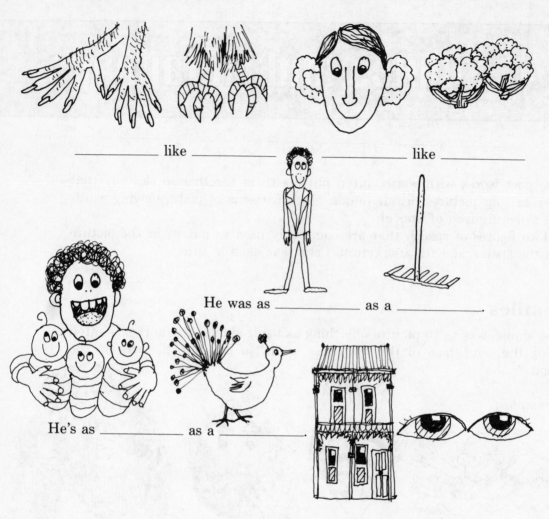

_____ like _____   _____ like _____

He was as _____ as a _____.

He's as _____ as a _____.

The _____ were like _____.

That _____ goes like a _____.

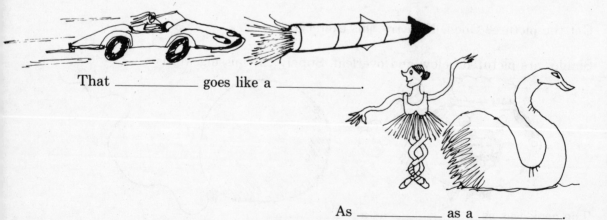

As _____ as a _____.

Simile Practice

There are many familiar similes in which comparisons are made with (a) animals and birds, and (b) things or objects.

Using the boxes, complete the similes by filling in (a) the animals or birds, and (b) the things or objects.

ANIMALS & BIRDS

monkeys	leech	owl	lamb	mule
lark	hyena	ox	wolf	ostrich
elephants	coot	hawk	sheep	duck

(1)   He laughs like a ....
(2)   She's as hungry as a ....
(3)   He waddled like a ....
(4)   He's as bald as a ....
(5)   She was as gentle as a ....
(6)   The crowds poured into the oval like .... into a paddock.
(7)   She's as wise as an ....
(8)   He clung like a .... to his surfboard.
(9)   He's as strong as an ....
(10) She wouldn't listen, she was like an .... with its head in the sand.
(11) She was as happy as a ....
(12) The players lumbered like .... through the mud to the finishing line.
(13) She had eyes like a ....
(14) They clung to the tree's branches, as agile as ....
(15) She's as obstinate as a ....

THINGS/OBJECTS

berries	ABC	arrow	lead	whip
leaf	wind	ghost	honey	silk	thieves
feather	mustard	hammer	furnace

(1) It was as heavy as ....
(2) You look as white as a ....
(3) The sprinters ran like the ....
(4) With a fist like a .... he pounded the desk.
(5) They're as keen as ....
(6) She's as sweet as ....
(7) They've been out in the sun all day and now they're as brown as ....
(8) She's as light as a ....
(9) His voice cracked out like a ....
(10) As straight as an ...., the road ran from the coast to the hills.
(11) He was so cold that he was trembling like a ....
(12) Allow me, it's as easy as ....
(13) Out beyond the shade, it's as hot as a ....
(14) It's as smooth as ....
(15) They're as thick as ....

A Simile Poem

Here is a poem about a greyhound. Read it through to yourself.

HOW A GOOD GREYHOUND IS SHAPED

A head like a snake, a neck like a drake,
A back like a beam, a belly like a bream,
A foot like a cat, a tail like a rat.

ANONYMOUS

Did you notice that it was completely made up of similes? Now try to write an animal poem of your own, also made up of similes. You may like to use the following model to write your simile poem.

HOW A GOOD .... IS SHAPED

A head like a ...., a neck like a ....
A nose like a ...., a mouth like a ....
An ear like a ...., a body like a ....

A great deal of good fun can be had by writing simile poems about people you know. Try some and read them aloud to the class, without revealing the names of the persons you write about.

Metaphors

The metaphor goes a step further than the simile and instead of asking us to picture one thing as *being like* another, we are asked to picture one thing as *being* (or 'merging with') another.

Example: Have you ever thought, looking up at the sky, that the moon moving through the clouds looked rather like a ship sailing through the heavy seas? The idea is pictured in this simile:

The moon was like a ghostly galleon tossed upon cloudy seas.

But the metaphor goes a step further and *merges* the two pictures:

The moon was a ghostly galleon tossed upon cloudy seas.

Two Metaphor Poems

Here is a very unusual poem. It is a metaphor, a rather long one, in which Jane takes on the appearance and habits of a bird.

MY SISTER JANE

And I say nothing — no, not a word
About our Jane. Haven't you heard?
She's a bird, a bird, a bird, a bird.
Oh it never would do to let folks know
My sister's nothing but a great big crow.

Each day (we daren't send her to school)
She pulls on stockings of thick blue wool
To make her pin crow legs look right,
Then fits a wig of curls on tight,
And dark spectacles — a huge pair
To cover her very crowy stare.
Oh it never would do to let folks know
My sister's nothing but a great big crow.

When visitors come she sits upright
(With her wings and her tail tucked out of sight).
They think her queer but extremely polite.
Then when the visitors have gone
She whips out her wings and with her wig on
Whirls through the house at the height of your head —
Duck, duck, or she'll knock you dead.
Oh it never would do to let folks know
My sister's nothing but a great big crow.

At meals whatever she sees she'll stab it —
Because she's a crow and that's a crow habit.
My mother says 'Jane! Your manners! Please!'
Then she'll sit quietly on the cheese,
Or play the piano nicely by dancing on the keys —
Oh it never would do to let folks know
My sister's nothing but a great big crow.

TED HUGHES

My Sister Jane — A bird or a Jane?
(1) Try to draw a picture of Jane as the poet has described her.
(2) What parts of Jane's body are similar to those of a crow?
(3) What are some of the things that Jane does which, metaphorically speaking, make her a crow?
(4) Do you think that by using a metaphor of a bird to describe Jane, the poet is being cruel in any way?
(5) In what ways do you think the poet could be exaggerating in his description of Jane?

You'll see that the subject of the following poem is — a poem! The whole of 'How to Eat a Poem' is a startling metaphor. Read it and find out what the metaphor is.

HOW TO EAT A POEM

Don't be polite.
Bite in.
Pick it up with your fingers and lick the juice that
    may run down your chin.
It is ready and ripe now, whenever you are.

You do not need a knife or fork or spoon
or plate or napkin or tablecloth.

For there is no core
or stem
or rind
or pit
or seed
or skin
to throw away.

EVE MERRIAM

Metaphors in the Comic Strips

Metaphors can be found in all types of writing — even in comic strips and cartoons! See how easily you can identify the metaphors in the following comic strips.

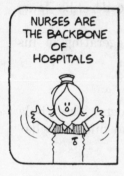

"A bit of a wet blanket, is he? Better invite him anyhow. With the bushfire season just starting, he might come in handy!"

A Mixture of Similes and Metaphors

Here's a poem, 'Concrete Mixers', with a good mixture of similes and metaphors. Copy the poem into your books. Put a single line under the similes and a double line under the metaphors. Then draw the concrete mixers as they are described in the poem.

CONCRETE MIXERS

The drivers are washing the concrete mixers;
Like elephant tenders they hose them down.
Tough grey-skinned monsters standing ponderous,
Elephant-bellied and elephant-nosed,
Standing in muck up to their wheel-caps,
Like rows of elephants, tail to trunk.
Their drivers perch on their backs like mahouts,
Sending the sprays of water up.
They rid the trunk-like trough of concrete,
Direct the spray to the bulging sides,
Turn and start the monsters moving.
   Concrete mixers
   Move like elephants
   Bellow like elephants
   Spray like elephants,
Concrete mixers are urban elephants,
Their trunks are raising a city.

PATRICIA HUBBELL

Simile or Metaphor?

Decide which of the following expressions are similes and which are metaphors. A good way of doing this is to draw up two columns in your book, headed SIMILES and METAPHORS, and then simply to write each of the expressions under one or other of the headings.

(1)   Her eyes they shone like diamonds.
(2)   The moon's a balloon
(3)   Suddenly she arched her back like a horseshoe.
(4)   Silver-hatted mushrooms
(5)   At the end of the street lives small Miss Wing,
      A feathery, fluttery bird of a thing.
(6)   The truck flew down the empty highway.
(7)   Your ears pop like champagne corks.
(8)   His eyes peer from his hair and beard like mice from a load of hay.
(9)   The sea is a mirror for the clouds.
(10) The shadows were as black as sin.
(11) The wind was a whip that cracked over our heads.
(12) I have seen old ships sail like swans asleep.
(13) He's as wild as a dingo.
(14) The stars are pinpricks in the velvet of the night sky.
(15) She came — and then, ghost-like, vanished.
(16) Enthusiasm is your key to success.
(17) She's as pretty as a picture.
(18) Watch out — it's that bullet-headed man again!
(19) They were as quiet as mice.
(20) Teeth like pearls
(21) The road arrowed into the hills.
(22) Education is your passport to satisfying employment.

2. People

THE POSTMAN

Satchel on hip
the postman goes
from doorstep to doorstep
and stooping sows

each letterbox
with seed. His right
hand all the morning makes
the same half circle. White

seed he scatters,
a fistful of
featureless letters
pregnant with ruin or love.

I watch him zig-
zag down the street
dipping his hand in that big
bag, sowing the cool, neat

envelopes which
make *twenty-one*
unaccountably rich,
twenty-two an orphan.

I cannot see
them but I know
others are watching. We
stoop in a row

(as he turns away),
straighten and stand
weighing and delaying
the future in one hand.

JON STALLWORTHY

The Postman — Explanations required

(1) Explain what is meant by 'sows each letterbox with seed'. What is this figure of speech called?

(2) How is it that the letters can be described as 'featureless'?

(3) How can a letter be 'pregnant with ruin or love'?

(4) What are 'twenty-one' and 'twenty-two'? Why are they in italic type?

(5) What feature of letters is being emphasised in the stanza which begins, 'envelopes which . . .'?

(6) What are the various persons doing when they 'stand weighing and delaying the future in one hand'?

(7) What is the effect of the short, broken lines? Do they contribute in any way to our view of the subject of this poem?

Inventors sometimes seem a little crazy!

Here's an inventor who's a little different — Uncle Dan!

UNCLE DAN

My Uncle Dan's an inventor, you may think that's very fine,
You may wish he was your Uncle instead of being mine —
If he wanted he could make a watch that bounces when it drops,
He could make a helicopter out of string and bottle tops
Or any really useful thing you can't get in the shops.

But Uncle Dan has other ideas:
The bottomless glass for ginger beers,
The toothless saw that's safe for the tree,
A special word for a spelling bee
(Like Lionocerangoutangadder),
Or the roll-uppable rubber ladder,
The mystery pie that bites when it's bit —
My Uncle Dan invented it.

My Uncle Dan sits in his den inventing night and day.
His eyes peer from his hair and beard like mice from a load of hay.
And does he make the shoes that will go walks without your feet?
A shrinker to shrink instantly the elephants you meet?
A carver that just carves from the air steaks cooked and ready to
    eat?

No, no, he has other intentions —
Only perfectly useless inventions:
Glassless windows (they never break)
A medicine to cure the earthquake
The unspillable screwed-down cup,
The stairs that go neither down nor up,
The door you simply paint on a wall —
Uncle Dan invented them all.

TED HUGHES

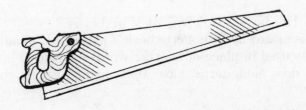

SILHOUETTE HEELS

I have me a place which is all me own
When me old man dags me
    and me mother — she can't stop her moan
I put on me silhouette heels and go
    clicking down the stairs.

At the bus stop I pay me fare — one (sh) and six (d)
And I go find me a seat at the top
Where the wind changes me from a dumb sheila
    with good legs to *someone*.
My mind is free to think and dream;
I become a princess, Sophia Loren, the Queen;
    — not myself.

Suddenly the bus stops — I get off and walk through
    the town
And I can't help myself from wiggling and noticing
    all the eyes on me
And if there's a 'nicee' I might give him a 'come-on'.
I drop in at the pub and have me a few
But soon it's time for me, again, to get home.

Again I pay me one and six and sit in the top — my
    special place
where I can wish, dream, I was someone.

I get off at my stop
And go clicking up the stairs in my silhouette heels
Me old man will dag me
    and me mother won't stop her moan;
And maybe again I'll go to me special place —
    to dream, to wish . . .

IRENE KOLTUNIEWICZ

Silhouette Heels — Looking at words

(1)   What is meant by 'silhouette heels'? Is this just a malapropism (a word wrongly used in place of another word) for *stiletto* heels? What associations does 'silhouette' have that might also fit the subject of this poem?

(2) What do you think 'dags' means? Is it all right to use slang like this in a poem? What guidelines would you offer to someone who asked when it was correct to use slang and when it wasn't?

(3) What are some of the things that happen in the girl's imagination when she 'becomes a princess'?

(4) What is meant by a 'nicee' and what is a 'come-on'?

(5) Suggest an explanation for the fact that the girl sometimes uses 'me' ('me mother') and sometimes uses 'my' ('my special place').

(6) What does the language suggest to *you* about this girl?

I DON'T WANT TO GO TO SCHOOL MUM

I don't want to go to school Mum
I want to stay at home with my duck.
I'd rather stay at home with you Mum,
And hit the skirting board with my truck.
Don't make me go to school today Mum,
I'll sit here quiet on the stairs
Or I'll sit underneath the table
Scratching all the varnish off the chairs.

I don't want to go to school Mum
When I could be underneath your feet.
It's shopping day and we could go together
Taking twice as long to get to Regent Street.
And every time you stop to talk to someone
I won't let you concentrate, no fear,
I'll be jumping up and down beside you
Shouting, 'Can I have some sweets Mum?' in your ear.

Or how about me doing a bit of painting?
Or what about a bit of cutting out?
Or sitting in the open bedroom window,
Body in and legs sticking out?
Or what about us going up the park Mum?
Or how about me sitting at the sink?
Or what about me making you a cake Mum?
And Mum. Hey Mum. Mum can I have a drink?

And Mum, Mum what's that at the bottom of the cupboard?
And Mum, what's in the bag you put down there?
And hey Mum watch me jump straight off the sofa,
And Mum, whose dog is that stood over there?
What you doing Mum? Peeling potatoes?
Sit me on the drainer watching you
I wouldn't *mind* me trousers getting wet Mum.
Oh I aren't half fed up. What can I do?

What time is Daddy coming home Mum?
What's in that long packet? Sausagemeat?
How long is it before he comes Mum?
And Mum. Hey Mum. What can I have to eat?
Oh sorry Mum! I've upset me Ribena.
Oh look! It's making quite a little pool.
Hey Mum, hey, where we going in such a hurry?
Oh Mum! Hey Mum, you're taking me to SCHOOL!

PAM AYRES

Feelings about school
(1)   How does the child feel about school?
(2)   Why does the child think that home is a better place to be?
(3)   What feelings are being expressed by the child at the end of the fourth stanza?
(4)   Outline the feelings Mum has which prompt her to drag her child off to school.

Creating
Imagine that you are this child's mother. Write your own humorous poem or story explaining why you want your son/daughter to go to school. Start it off with:

'I want you to go to school, son/daughter ...'

OR

'I don't want you to stay at home son/daughter ..

AFRICAN BEGGAR

Sprawled in the dust outside the Syrian store,
a target for small children, dogs and flies,
a heap of verminous rags and matted hair,
he watches us with cunning, reptile eyes,
his noiseless, smallpoxed face creased in a sneer.

Sometimes he shows his yellow stumps of teeth
and whines for alms, perceiving that we bear
the curse of pity; a grotesque mask of death,
with hands like claws about his begging-bowl.

But often he is lying all alone
within the shadow of a crumbling wall,
lost in the trackless jungle of his pain,
clutching the pitiless red earth in vain
and whimpering like a stricken animal.

RAYMOND TONG

African Beggar — Emotions

(1) Which of the following words do you feel comes closest to describing the poet's emotions?

**sympathy, anger, revulsion, dislike,
irritation, compassion, detachment, pity**

(2) Now try to find evidence in the poem to support your choice in the question above.

(3) What would your own feelings have been towards this beggar?

This narrative poem from early last century records the daring abduction of Ellen by the young Scottish lord, Lochinvar. The strong lively rhythm of the poem and the appeal of its exciting and romantic theme have made it popular with all generations since.

LOCHINVAR

O, young Lochinvar is come out of the west,
Through all the wide Border[1] his steed was the best;
And save his good broadsword he weapons had none,
He rode all unarm'd and he rode all alone.
So faithful in love and so dauntless in war,
There never was knight like the young Lochinvar.

He staid not for brake, and he stopp'd not for stone,
He swam the Eske river where ford there was none;
But ere he alighted at Netherby gate,
The bride had consented,[2] the gallant came late:
For a laggard in love, and a dastard in war
Was to wed the fair Ellen of brave Lochinvar.

So boldly he enter'd the Netherby Hall,
Among the bride's-men, and kinsmen, and brothers, and all:
Then spoke the bride's father, his hand on his sword
(For the poor craven bridegroom said never a word)
'O come ye in peace here, or come ye in war,
Or to dance at our bridal, young Lord Lochinvar?'

'I long woo'd your daughter, my suit you denied;
Love swells like the Solway, but ebbs like the tide —
And now am I come, with this lost love of mine,
To lead but one measure, drink one cup of wine.
There are maidens in Scotland more lovely by far,
That would gladly be bride to the young Lochinvar.'

The bride kiss'd the goblet: the knight took it up.
He quaff'd off the wine, and he threw down the cup.
She look'd down to blush, and she look'd up to sigh,
With a smile on her lips, and a tear in her eye.
He took her soft hand, ere her mother could bar —
'Now tread we a measure!' said young Lochinvar.

1 *Border:* The country around the border between England and Scotland.
2 *had consented:* i.e. to marry somebody else.

So stately his form, and so lovely her face,
That never a hall such a galliard[3] did grace;
While her mother did fret, and her father did fume,
And the bridegroom stood dangling his bonnet and plume;
And the bride-maidens whisper'd, "Twere better by far,
To have matched our fair cousin with young Lochinvar.'

One touch to her hand, and one word in her ear,
When they reach'd the hall-door, and the charger stood near;
So light to the croupe[4] the fair lady he swung,
So light to the saddle before her he sprung!
'She is won! we are gone, over bank, bush, and scaur;
They'll have fleet steeds that follow,' quoth young Lochinvar.

There was mounting 'mong Graemes of the Netherby clan;
Forsters, Fenwicks, and Musgraves, they rode and they ran;
There was racing and chasing on Cannobie Lee,
But the lost bride of Netherby ne'er did they see.
So daring in love, and so dauntless in war,
Have ye e'er heard a gallant like young Lochinvar?

SIR WALTER SCOTT

3 *galliard:* a type of dance.
4 *croupe:* place behind the saddle.

Lochinvar — Finding the clues

(1) What clues can you find to suggest that Lochinvar was (a) fearless, and (b) determined?

(2) What clues show that Ellen really loved Lochinvar?

(3) What clues can you find that they had been prevented from marrying?

(4) What clues show that Lochinvar had deliberately set out to deceive Ellen's father? Do you think Lochinvar was justified in doing what he did? Give your reasons.

(5) What clues reveal that the bridegroom was cowardly?

(6) What clues tell us that the fair Ellen agreed to go along with Lochinvar?

(7) What clues inform us that Ellen and Lochinvar made a very handsome couple on the dance floor?

(8) What clues show that Ellen's mother and father were worried by Lochinvar's dancing with Ellen?

(9) What clues indicate that Lochinvar had prepared to make a quick exit?

(10) What clues can you find that Ellen's relatives were determined to pursue Lochinvar?

MY BUS CONDUCTOR

My bus conductor tells me
he only has one kidney
and that may soon go on strike
through overwork.
Each bus ticket
takes on now a different shape
and texture.
He holds a ninepenny single
as if it were a rose
and puts the shilling in his bag
as a child into a gasmeter.

His thin lips
have no quips
for fat factory girls
and he ignores
the drunk who snores
and the old man who talks to himself
and gets off at the wrong stop.
He goes gently to the bedroom
of the bus
to collect
and watch familiar shops and pubs pass by
(perhaps for the last time?).
The same old streets look different now
more distinct
as through new glasses.
And the sky
Was it ever so blue?

And all the time
deep down in the deserted bus shelter of his mind
he thinks about his journey nearly done.
One day he'll clock on and never clock off
or clock off and never clock on.

ROGER McGOUGH

My Bus Conductor — Understanding and responding

(1) What is meant by 'one kidney ... may soon go on strike through overwork'?
(2) What evidence can you find to show that the bus conductor is a changed man?
(3) Explain how a child would put a coin into a gasmeter. What does this image convey about the way the conductor handles the fares now?
(4) What has changed this bus conductor so much?
(5) What is the 'journey' to which his mind constantly returns?
(6) How effectively has the poet created a mood for you in this poem? What is this mood, and what feelings have been aroused?

Sometimes a little humour can hide some fairly strong feelings. In the following poem, how does the poet *really* feel about his former bank manager? The word 'former' is a clue, telling us ... what?

A CURSE ON MY FORMER BANK MANAGER

May your computer twitch every time it remembers money
until the twitches mount and become a mechanical ache
and may the ache increase until the tapes begin to scream
and may the pus of data burst from its metal skin

and just before the downpour of molten aluminium
may you be preening in front of your computer
and may you be saying to your favourite millionaire
yes it cost nine hundred thousand but it repays every penny

and may the hundred-mile tape which records my debts spring out
like a supersonic two-dimensional boa-constrictor
and may it slip under your faultless collar and surround your
   hairless neck
and may it tighten and tighten until it has repaid everything
   I owe you

ADRIAN MITCHELL

Two curses

(1) What do you imagine to be the incident behind this poem? What has the bank manager done to annoy the poet?
(2) Imagine that you have just tried to trade-in your second-hand car on a new one, and that the salesman offered what you consider a pathetic deal. Write a poem or story titled, 'A Curse on a Car Salesman'.

A *tall story* is one in which the exaggeration is so outrageous that it makes you want to laugh. Well, exaggeration goes wild in this poem.

MUMMY SLEPT LATE AND DADDY FIXED BREAKFAST

Daddy fixed breakfast.
He made us each a waffle.
It looked like gravel pudding.
It tasted something awful.

'Ha, ha,' he said, 'I'll try again.
This time I'll get it right.'
But what *I* got was in between
Bituminous and anthracite.[1]

'A little too well done? Oh well,
I'll have to start all over.'
That time what landed on my plate
Looked like a manhole cover.

I tried to cut it with a fork:
The fork gave off a spark.
I tried a knife and twisted it
Into a question mark.

I tried it with a hack-saw.
I tried it with a torch.
It didn't even make a dent.
It didn't even scorch.

The next time Dad gets breakfast
When Mummy's sleeping late,
I think I'll skip the waffles.
I'd sooner eat the plate!

JOHN CIARDI

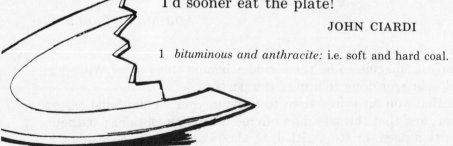

1 *bituminous and anthracite:* i.e. soft and hard coal.

THE SLAVE'S DREAM

Beside the ungathered rice he lay,
  His sickle in his hand;
His breast was bare, his matted hair
  Was buried in the sand.
Again, in the mist and shadow of sleep,
  He saw his Native Land.

Wide through the landscape of his dreams
  The lordly Niger flowed:
Beneath the palm-trees on the plain
  Once more a king he strode;
And heard the tinkling caravans
  Descend the mountain-road.

He saw once more his dark-eyed queen
  Among her children stand;
They clasped his neck, they kissed his cheeks,
  They held him by the hand! —
A tear burst from the sleeper's lids,
  And fell into the sand.

And then at furious speed he rode
  Along the Niger's bank;
His bridle-reins were golden chains,
  And, with a martial clank,
At each leap he could feel his scabbard of steel
  Smiting his stallion's flank.

Before him, like a blood-red flag,
  The bright flamingoes flew;
From morn till night he followed their flight,
  O'er the plains where the tamarind grew,
Till he saw the roofs of Caffre huts,
  And the ocean rose to view.

At night he heard the lion roar,
  And the hyena scream,
And the river-horse, as he crushed the reeds
  Beside some hidden stream;
And it passed, like a glorious roll of drums,
  Through the triumph of his dream.

The forests, with their myriad tongues,
  Shouted of liberty;
And the Blast of the Desert cried aloud,
  With a voice so wild and free,
That he started in his sleep and smiled
  At their tempestuous glee.

He did not feel the driver's whip,
  Nor the burning heat of day;
For Death had illumined the Land of Sleep,
  And his lifeless body lay
A worn-out fetter, that the soul
  Had broken and thrown away!

HENRY WADSWORTH LONGFELLOW

The Slave's Dream — Thinking it over

(1) What is there at the start of the poem to suggest that the slave still has work to do?
(2) In former years, what position had this slave held?
(3) Identify at least two visible reactions that you might have seen in the sleeping slave had you been watching him.
(4) Explain why the flamingoes were 'like a blood-red flag'.
(5) Identify three animals native to the slave's homeland.
(6) Explain what is meant by
    'The forests, with their myriad tongues,
    Shouted of liberty;'
(7) What happens to the slave at the end of the poem?
(8) Write down your reaction to this poem, explaining why you like or dislike it.

This is a very sad poem about poor Butch Weldy. As well as being sad it shows that, in life, justice is not always on the side of the innocent.

BUTCH WELDY

After I got religion and steadied down
They gave me a job in the canning works,
And every morning I had to fill
The tank in the yard with gasoline,
That fed the blow-fires in the sheds
To heat the soldering irons.

And I mounted a rickety ladder to do it,
Carrying buckets full of the stuff.
One morning, as I stood there pouring,
The air grew still and seemed to heave,
And I shot up as the tank exploded,
And down I came with both legs broken,
And my eyes burned crisp as a couple of eggs.
For someone left a blow-fire going,
And something sucked the flame in the tank.
The Circuit Judge said whoever did it
Was a fellow-servant of mine, and so
Old Rhodes' son didn't have to pay me.
And I sat on the witness stand as blind
As Jack the Fiddler, saying over and over,
'I didn't know him at all.'

EDGAR LEE MASTERS

Butch Weldy — Talking points
(1) Did you agree with the judge's decision that Old Rhodes' son didn't have to pay Butch? Why?
(2) Can you explain why Butch kept saying over and over, 'I didn't know him at all'?
(3) Do you think belonging to a union could have helped Butch?
(4) Have you encountered a lack of justice at school or somewhere else? Give details to the class.
(5) Have you encountered stupid regulations, rules or laws? Describe one of them to the class.

It isn't always possessions and status that make a man a prince. Often, a person's actions are what really counts.

A PRINCE OF MEN

I drove today behind a garbage truck,
Not a modern one — an open one.
In all the waste,
Holding firmly to the upright side
Of one wall of the truck,
A Negro worker stood.
Cold, dripping rain splattered

All around him, all over him.
His clothes were soggy,
Soaked through.
No raincoat. No rainhat.
Only a ragged cap,
A blob of soggy cloth upon his head.
Yet, he was concerned for me.
He noticed that the truck was slowing
My progress;
My progress in the new car,
Warmly heated from the buzzing heater,
Sheltered by the shiny roof above.
He smiled and looked ahead
To see if I could pass
And waved the friendliest wave
To say, 'It's okay. There's no one coming.
    Go on! Pass! Sorry to hold you up!'
As I passed, I wondered.
Would I have cared if anyone was slowed up
In that shiny, heated car?
What prince of men was this?
How did he learn such kindness —
From waste and rain and coldness ... from
Other men?
Would I have waved ... or spit?

                              JACK NOFFSINGER

A Prince of Men — Understanding
(1)   What is there about the Negro to suggest that he is of a fairly low social status?
(2)   How does the poet's position contrast with that of the Negro?
(3)   What makes the poet call the Negro a 'prince of men'?
(4)   The poet is left asking two questions after this incident. What are they?

Appreciating
(5)   How does the description of the Negro, starting with 'Cold, dripping rain ...', make you feel about this man?
(6)   How successfully does the poet convey to you the impact that this incident had on him?
(7)   What is there about this poem that makes you feel it is successful or unsuccessful?

3. Sound-Words

There are many words in English that actually suggest the sound of the action they are referring to. Words such as *growl, purr, moo, crunch, squelch, drip, flop, bang, slurp* and *thud* are just a few of the many sound-words we come across every day. The formal name for this occurrence is **onomato-poeia**. Poets use sound-words more than most people. Can you suggest why? Read through the poem 'Company Manners'. Most of the lines contain sound-words.

COMPANY MANNERS

Hands off the tablecloth
don't rumble belly
don't grab for grub
don't slurp the soup
don't crumble the crackers
don't mash the mushrooms
don't mush the potatoes
don't stab the steak
don't slap the saltshaker
don't pill the bread
don't swill the sauce
don't ooze the mayonnaise
don't slop the slaw
don't spatter the ketchup
don't gulp the olives

don't spit the pips
don't finger the lettuce
don't dribble the dressing
don't chomp the celery
don't gobble the cobbler
don't guzzle the fizz
swallow don't swig
don't smack your lips
pat with a napkin
daintily dab
quietly quaff
fastidious sip
and gracefully sample
a nibbling tidbit.

EVE MERRIAM

Do the sound-words in this poem remind you of the sounds heard at the table while people are eating? Pick out two or three of the sound-words which you think are particularly suitable and explain why.

Sound-Words in the Comic Strips

If you look through the comic strips in your local papers you'll find that cartoonists often use onomatopoeic words or sound-words. There is a very good reason for this. The cartoonist, like the poet, is trying to give his pictures life, and also to say as much as possible in a limited space. Now read through these comic strips and see whether you can answer the questions concerning the sound-words.

ST PIPS — By Neil Matterson

HAGAR THE HORRIBLE By Dik Browne

Questions

(1) Write down the sound-word in *St Pips*. What action is this word representing?

(2) Look at the dog sound-words in *Fred Basset*. Write down all three of them and underline the loudest one.

(3) What action does the sound-word 'thwak!' represent in *Stanley*?

(4) What action does the sound-word 'slurp!' represent in the *Hagar the Horrible* cartoon?

So you can see that with one simple sound-word a cartoonist can seize the attention of the reader. Start collecting cartoon strips with sound-words in them for your class notice-board.

More Sounds and Noises

THE WASHING MACHINE

It goes fwunkety,
   then slunkety,
as the washing goes around.

The water spluncheses,
   and it sluncheses,
as the washing goes around.

As you pick it out it splocheses,
   and it flocheses,
as the washing goes around.

But at the end it schlopperies,
   and then flopperies,
as the washing stops going around.

JEFFREY DAVIES

The Washing Machine — and your own sound-words

(1)   The poet has made up eight sound-words of his own. There are two in each stanza. See whether you can find them and write them down.

(2)   Now try your hand at writing down a word (or two) representing the sounds made by each of the following:
   (a) someone walking on a sheet of corrugated iron
   (b) a vacuum-cleaner sucking up the dirt
   (c) a fisherman throwing out his rod
   (d) someone trying to start a car which has a flat battery
   (e) chalk on a blackboard
   (f) sausages cooking in a pan
   (g) someone walking through thick mud
   (h) a fire burning briskly
   (i) a kettle boiling
   (j) a cat drinking milk
   (k) a car running into another car
   (l) a glass dropping on concrete
   (m) someone eating potato-chips
   (n) cats fighting
   (o) dry leaves being blown along the ground by the wind

(p) hitting a tennis ball
(q) a rocket taking off
(r) a piece of very ripe fruit hitting a wall
(s) a can of shaken-up soft-drink being opened
(t) a dentist drilling into your tooth
(u) a balloon bursting
(v) a noisy lawnmower
(w) a typewriter being used by an expert — and then by a non-expert

NOISE

I like noise.
The whoop of a boy, the thud of a hoof,
The rattle of rain on a galvanized roof,
The hubbub of traffic, the roar of a train,
The throb of machinery numbing the brain,
The rush of the wind, a door on the slam,
The switching of wires in an overhead tram,
The boom of the thunder, the crash of the waves,
The din of a river that races and raves,
The crack of a rifle, the clank of a pail,
The strident tattoo of a swift-slapping sail —
Arises a gamut of soul-stirring joys.
I like noise.

JESSIE POPE

Over to you

Now trying writing poems of your own, by filling in the spaces in the three blocks below. The first two spaces in each block have been completed as examples.

I like sounds.
The swish.......... of the ..wind...
The .... of ....
The .... of ....
The .... of ....
The .... of ....
I like sounds.

I like music.
The throb.......... of guitars.......
The .... of ....
The .... of ....
The .... of ....
The .... of ....
I like music.

I like sport.
The ..splash...... of .water......
The .... of ....
The .... of ....
The .... of ....
The .... of ....
I like sport.

Now attempt an 'I don't like' poem of your own.

4. Animals and Others

You've all had experiences with dogs. Mostly these experiences are pleasant, but sometimes things go wrong. 'Puppy Problems' is a tale of woe about owning a new dog.

PUPPY PROBLEMS

I bought myself a puppy
And I hoped in time he might
Become my friend and ward off
Things that go bump in the night,
So I put him in a shoe box
And at home I took him out,
And then began to learn
What owning puppies is about.

I tried so hard to love him
And I didn't rave and shout
As he bit into the sofa
And he dragged the stuffing out.
I *gave* him things to chew
But soon I couldn't fail to see
That he liked the things he *found*
More than the things supplied by me.

He frayed my lovely carpet
That I'd saved my pennies for,
And when he wasn't chewing
He was weeing on the floor.
Nor did he spare the table leg
That came in for a gnaw,
Though I told him off the message
Never seemed to reach his jaw.

We laboured at the gardening,
Me and my little pup.
At two I planted flowers
And at four he dug them up.
He liked to dig, he'd bury bones
And pat it down so neat,
And then he'd rush indoors
As clods of mud flew off his feet.

I bought a book on training
And I read it all one night,
And when we set off out
I really thought we'd got it right,
With titbits in my coat
To give him once he got the knack,
But he didn't so I couldn't
So *I* ate them coming back.

When I commanded 'Heel!'
He never seemed to take the point
But galloped on half-strangled,
Tugging my arm out of joint.
He jumped up people's clothes,
The cleaning bills I had to pay!
And when I shouted 'Here!'
He turned and ran the other way.

One day I drove him over
And I gave him to my Dad
Who welcomed him and trained him,
But it left me very sad.
So I thought I'd let you know
In case a pup's in store for you
That it's very wise indeed
To have a Dad who likes dogs too.

PAM AYRES

Puppy Problems — In your opinion

(1) People keep pets for all kinds of reasons. Why did Pam Ayres buy her puppy?

(2) How does the poet show that she had good self-control?

(3) How did the puppy misbehave while he was in the house?

(4) Find evidence to show that the puppy misbehaved in the garden as well.

(5) How did the puppy react to its first owner's training methods?

(6) There are dog-owners who will suggest that Pam Ayres was responsible for some of the bad habits of her puppy. Would you agree? Why?

(7) What would you have done if you had owned her puppy?

(8) Why do you think her Dad was able to train the puppy, while Pam Ayres herself was not?

In your experience

(1) Tell the class about one of the pets you have owned. Describe (a) your pet's appearance and (b) some of the unusual things it did; then (c) explain why you liked it and (d) recall how other people felt about it.

(2) Some people would think that the poet's problems with her puppy are funny. Do you agree?

ADVANTAGE OF FROGS OVER DOGS

I cannot say why Mrs Bray
is so wrapped up with dogs,
when her garden pond and the ditch beyond
are thick on the brim with frogs.

A frog that's green and large and clean,
and disciplined as well,
can be trained to hop to the corner shop
and answer the front-door bell.

When Mrs Bray goes far away
it costs a mint to board her dogs,
but a compost heap, with things that creep,
is all that you need for frogs.

COLIN BINGHAM

Poet's Corner

Dear Girls and Boys,

Please do not think, when you read 'Advantage of Frogs over Dogs', that I would always choose a frog instead of a dog. But the ordinary frog — not the cane toad — has qualities that you and I should recognise.

When I was a small boy in the Queensland outback I lived near a big swamp divided by a road. When the rains came and the swamp was flooded, the frogs at night formed themselves into a huge choir. The tenors and the sopranos were on one side of the road and the baritones and contraltos on the other. No one could guess just where the conductor was, but he was able, in some remarkable way, to stop and start his singers with perfect precision. I used to lie awake listening to them, especially when they sang, 'Hail, hail, O Mighty Storm'.

Years later, when I was a young married man in Brisbane, my wife and I sometimes listened to classical radio programmes in the evening. (There was no TV then.) Nearly always we were joined by a big green frog who came to the open door leading from a verandah. We noticed a special gleam in his eyes when a Beethoven symphony was played.

So you must see why I have written in a kindly way about frogs answering the doorbell and hopping to the corner shop.

Yours pleasantly,
Colin Bingham.

The death of a person or animal we love is usually a difficult emotional experience. This poet does not use a lot of words to tell us how he cared about his dog — we can *feel* the strength of his love. Read the poem through and then discuss the questions that follow.

OLD DOG

Toward the last in the morning she could not
get up, even when I rattled her pan.
I helped her into the yard, but she stumbled
and fell. I knew it was time.

The last night a mist drifted over the fields;
in the morning she would not raise her head —
the far, clear mountains we had walked
surged back to mind.

We looked a slow bargain: our days together
were the ones we already had.
I gave her something the vet had given,
and patted her still, a good last friend.

WILLIAM STAFFORD

Old Dog — Questions for discussion

(1) How *does* the poet convey to us his love for this dog?
(2) What are the *meaning* and the *effect* of 'I knew it was time.'?
(3) How does the poet draw comfort in the last hours of his friend's life?

'Sunning' is another poem about an old dog, yet it is quite different from 'Old Dog'. In 'Sunning' the poet tries to enter the experience of an old dog lying in the sun. The poem's rhythm is relaxed, almost lazy. The rhymes are of an ordinary, 'nothing-fancy' type. The poem is built from a few simple observations — a half-opened winking eye, a scratch, a whimper — and a little poetic imagination.

SUNNING

Old Dog lay in the summer sun
Much too lazy to rise and run.
He flapped an ear
At a buzzing fly.
He winked a half-opened
Sleepy eye.
He scratched himself
On an itching spot,
As he dozed on the porch
Where the sun was hot.
He whimpered a bit
From force of habit
While he lazily dreamed
Of chasing a rabbit.
But Old Dog happily lay in the sun
Much too lazy to rise and run.

JAMES TIPPETT

Try your hand

Write a poem similar in style to 'Sunning'. Choose one of the following subjects.

- a baby lying asleep in its cot
- a tiger lying asleep in its cage
- a shark resting at the bottom of an aquarium
- a kitten asleep against its mother

A CAT

She had a name among the children;
But no one loved though someone owned
Her, locked her out of doors at bedtime
And had her kittens duly drowned.

In Spring, nevertheless, this cat
Ate blackbirds, thrushes, nightingales,
And birds of bright voice and plume and flight,
As well as scraps from neighbours' pails.

I loathed and hated her for this;
One speckle on a thrush's breast
Was worth a million such; and yet
She lived long, till God gave her rest.

EDWARD THOMAS

A Cat — Questions to think about

Different animals inspire different reactions or feelings in people.

(1) How does the poet feel about this cat?
(2) What, in particular, makes him feel this way?
(3) What complaint does he seem to be making in the last couple of lines?

Try your hand

Write a short poem about a creature you dislike. Explain your feelings. Share your results around the class.

from REYNARD THE FOX

The fox was strong, he was full of running,
He could run for an hour and then be cunning,
But the cry behind him made him chill,
They were nearer now and they meant to kill.
They meant to run him until his blood
Clogged on his heart as his brush with mud,
Till his back bent up and his tongue hung flagging,
And his belly and brush were filthed with dragging.
Till he crouched stone-still, dead-beat and dirty,
With nothing but teeth against the thirty.
And all the way to that blinding end
He would meet with men and have none his friend:
Men to holloa and men to run him,
With stones to stagger and yells to stun him;
Men to head him, with whips to beat him,
Teeth to mangle, and mouths to eat him.
And all the way, that wild high crying
To cold his blood with the thought of dying,
The horn and the cheer, and the drum-like thunder
Of the horsehooves stamping the meadows under.
He upped his brush and went with a will
For the Sarsen Stones on Wan Dyke Hill ...

Seven Sarsens of granite grim,
As he ran them by they looked at him;
As he leaped the lip of their earthen paling
The hounds were gaining and he was failing.

He passed the Sarsens, he left the spur,
He pressed uphill to the blasted fir,
He slipped as he leaped the hedge; he slithered.
'He's mine,' thought Robin. 'He's done; he's dithered.'

At the second attempt he cleared the fence,
He turned half-right where the gorse was dense,
He was leading the hounds by a furlong clear.
He was past his best, but his earth was near.
He ran up gorse to the spring of the ramp,
The steep green wall of the dead men's camp,
He sidled up it and scampered down
To the deep green ditch of the Dead Men's Town.

Within, as he reached that soft green turf,
The wind, blowing lonely, moaned like surf,
Desolate ramparts rose up steep
On either side, for the ghosts to keep.
He raced the trench, past the rabbit warren,
Close-grown with moss which the wind made barren;
He passed the spring where the rushes spread,
And there in the stones was his earth ahead.
One last short burst upon failing feet —
There life lay waiting, so sweet, so sweet,
Rest in a darkness, balm for aches.

The earth was stopped. It was barred with stakes.

JOHN MASEFIELD

Reynard the Fox — Understanding

(1) What are some of the qualities of the fox that might help him to survive?

(2) What are some of the qualities attributed to the men who chase him?

(3) Even the Sarsen Stones appear to have feelings about this fox. How do they seem to view him?

(4) What action of the fox leads Robin to believe that the chase is over?

(5) What is the fox's home called?

(6) How does the fox attempt to throw the hunters off his track? Give one example.

Appreciating

(7) Why does the poet separate the last line?

(8) What feelings towards the fox does the poet seek to arouse in us? How does he do this?

(9) How does the rhythm suit the subject of this poem?

(10) What is the poet's purpose? Do you feel that he is successful in achieving this aim? Give your reasons.

TRAVELLING THROUGH THE DARK

Travelling through the dark I found a deer
dead on the edge of the Wilson River road.
It is usually best to roll them into the canyon:
that road is narrow; to swerve might make more dead.

By glow of the taillight I stumbled back of the car
and stood by the heap, a doe, a recent killing;
she had stiffened already, almost cold.
I dragged her off; she was large in the belly.

My fingers touching her side brought me the reason —
her side was warm; her fawn lay there waiting,
alive, still, never to be born.
Beside that mountain road I hesitated.

The car aimed ahead its lowered parking lights;
under the hood purred the steady engine.
I stood in the glare of the warm exhaust turning red;
around our group I could hear the wilderness listen.

I thought hard for us all — my only swerving —
then pushed her over the edge into the river.

WILLIAM STAFFORD

Travelling through the Dark — A lonely decision
(1) What is the most likely explanation for the presence of the dead deer?
(2) What does the poet mean by 'to swerve might make more dead'?
(3) Explain why the poet hesitates. Why has it suddenly become a big thing to push this deer into the canyon?
(4) 'The car aimed ahead ...' What does the car appear to be wanting to happen?
(5) 'I could hear the wilderness listen.' For what would it be listening?
(6) Why does the poet describe his stopping to think hard as a 'swerving'?
(7) The poem's title describes the man's journey in his car, but to what else might it be referring?
(8) What would you have done if you had been in the poet's position? Give your reasons.

'In Defence of Hedgehogs' is written almost as though a child were talking. It has an innocent, at times quite funny tone. This childlike approach to the subject is clever because it reminds us that children sometimes see simple truths more clearly than do adults.

IN DEFENCE OF HEDGEHOGS

I am very fond of hedgehogs
Which makes me want to say,
That I am struck with wonder,
How there's any left today,
For each morning as I travel
And no short distance that,
All I see are hedgehogs,
Squashed. And dead. And flat.

Now, hedgehogs are not clever,
No, hedgehogs are quite dim,
And when he sees your headlamps,
Well, it don't occur to him,
That the very wisest thing to do
Is up and run away,
No! he curls up in a stupid ball,
And no doubt starts to pray.

Well, motor cars do travel
At a most alarming rate,
And by the time you sees him,
It is very much too late,
And thus he gets a-squasho'd,
Unrecorded but for me,
With me pen and paper,
Sittin' in a tree.

It is statistically proven,
In chapter and in verse,
That in a car and hedgehog fight,
The hedgehog comes off worse,
When whistlin' down your prop shaft,
And bouncin' off your diff,
His coat of nice brown prickles
Is not effect-iff.

A hedgehog cannot make you laugh,
Whistle, dance or sing,
And he ain't much to look at,
And he don't make anything,
And in amongst his prickles,
There's fleas and bugs and that,
But there ain't no need to leave him,
Squashed. And dead. And flat.

Oh spare a thought for hedgehogs,
Spare a thought for me,
Spare a thought for hedgehogs,
As you drink your cup of tea,
Spare a thought for hedgehogs,
Hoverin' on the brinkt,
Spare a thought for hedgehogs,
Lest they become extinct.

PAM AYRES

In Defence of Hedgehogs — Reviewing the poem

(1)   What causes the poet to be 'struck with wonder'?
(2)   What kinds of hedgehogs does she see every morning as she travels?
(3)   What *should* a hedgehog do when it sees headlamps?
(4)   What does it *actually* do?
(5)   What is it about cars that makes them very dangerous for hedgehogs?
(6)   Give the double word that describes what happens when a car meets a hedgehog.
(7)   What do these lines mean?
      'When whistlin' down your prop shaft,
      And bouncin' off your diff,'
(8)   What unpleasant surprise could await you among the hedgehog's prickles?
(9)   The hedgehog, despite its dismal lack of personality, certainly does not deserve its all-too-common fate of being _____ and _____ and _____.
(10)   Why does Pam Ayres want us to spare a thought for the hedgehog?

Discussion Point

Many animal species are threatened with extinction. Why? What could you say about such animals — and the koala is one of them — that would cause people to 'spare a thought'?

The poet Don Marquis wrote a series of poems under the name of 'archy'. Archy is a very intelligent cockroach who satisfies his need to express himself in poetry by jumping up and down on the keyboard of Marquis's unattended typewriter. However, archy finds it impossible to produce capital letters, and, as for punctuation, he ignores that altogether. This explains the absence of both in archy's typing.

Archy refers to Don Marquis — his creator — as 'the boss', and all the boss has to do to find out 'how things look to a cockroach' is to roll a sheet of blank paper into his typewriter and take himself off for a while. Archy does the rest. He emerges from his home inside the typewriter, dances around on the keys and, when his poem is finished, scuttles back inside again. Here are two archy poems for you to read. In the first, 'the lesson of the moth', archy finds out why it is that moths always seem to be trying to burn themselves to death. . . .

THE LESSON OF THE MOTH

i was talking to a moth
the other evening
he was trying to break into
an electric light bulb
and fry himself on the wires

why do you fellows
pull this stunt i asked him
because it is the conventional
thing for moths or why
if that had been an uncovered
candle instead of an electric
light bulb you would
now be a small unsightly cinder
have you no sense

plenty of it he answered
but at times we get tired
of using it
we get bored with the routine
and crave beauty
and excitement
fire is beautiful
and we know that if we get
too close it will kill us

but what does that matter
it is better to be happy
for a moment
and be burned up with beauty
than to live a long time
and be bored all the while

so we wad all our life up
into one little roll
and then we shoot the roll
that is what life is for
it is better to be a part of beauty
for one instant and then cease to
exist than to exist forever
and never be a part of beauty
our attitude toward life
is come easy go easy

we are like human beings
used to be before they became
too civilized to enjoy themselves

and before i could argue him
out of his philosophy
he went and immolated[1] himself
on a patent cigar lighter
i do not agree with him
myself i would rather have
half the happiness and twice
the longevity[2]

but at the same time i wish
there was something i wanted
as badly as he wanted to fry himself

archy
(DON MARQUIS)

1 *immolated:* sacrificed.
2 *longevity:* long life.

The Lesson of the Moth — For you to draw
Draw a comic strip of archy the cockroach talking to the moth. Have them
using some of the words of the poem.

SMALL TALK

i went into the flea circus
on broadway the other day
and heard a lot of fleas
talking and bragging to each other
one flea had been over to the swell dog show
and was boasting that he had bit
a high priced thoroughbred dog
yeah says another flea
that is nothing to get so proud of
a thoroughbred dog tastes just like a mongrel
i should think you would be more democratic
than to brag about that
go and get a reputation
said a third flea
i went into a circus last spring and bit a lion
i completely conquered him
i made him whine and cringe
he did not bite me back
get out of my way
i am the flea that licked a lion
i said to myself probably
that lion didn't even know he had been bitten
some insects are just like human beings
small talk i said to myself
and went away from there

archy the cockroach
(DON MARQUIS)

Notice in these poems how normal punctuation has been disregarded by the poet. Read through 'small talk' and decide with the rest of the class where the normal punctuation marks would fall and what they should be.

Small Talk — Discussion
(1) What is the effect gained by omitting the punctuation? Why does the poet do this?
(2) Is this poem really intended to show us something about fleas or cockroaches? What is it really about? Be prepared to argue your point of view.

5. Shaped Poems

Students can derive a lot of enjoyment from writing their own shaped poems. The shape of the poem immediately shows the reader what the poem is about. Have a look at these shaped poems created by students of your own age.

I THINK I'M LOVELY

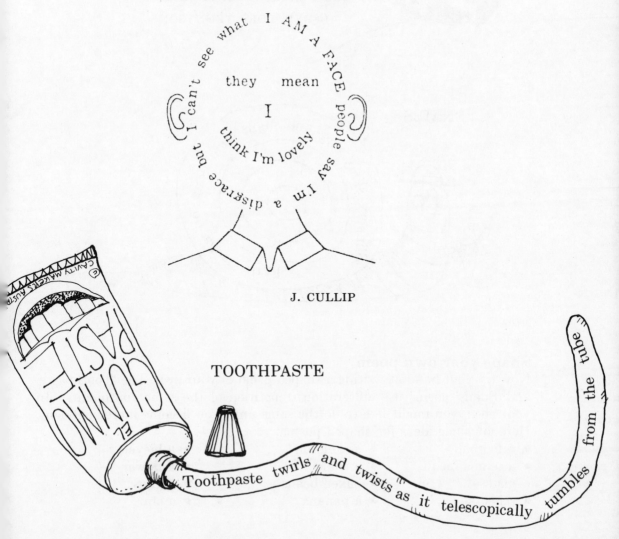

I AM A FACE

I can't see what they mean

they mean

I

think I'm lovely

people say I'm a disgrace but

J. CULLIP

TOOTHPASTE

Toothpaste twirls and twists as it telescopically tumbles from the tube

GUMMO PASTE

CAVITY MAKERS AUST.

THE EAGLE

He clasps the
crag with crooked
hands; Close to the
sun in lonely lands,
Ringed with the azure world
he stands.
The wrinkled sea
beneath him crawls;
He watches from his
mountain walls, And
like a thunderbolt he falls.

ALFRED, LORD TENNYSON

SNAILS

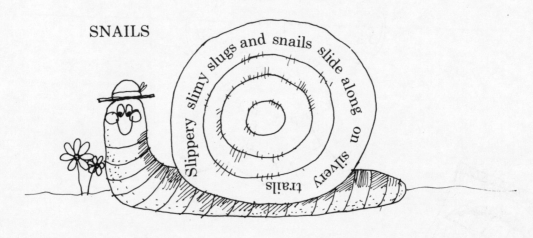

Slippery slimy slugs and snails slide along on silvery trails

Shape your own poem

Now try your hand at writing a shaped poem of your own. The 'Toothpaste'
and 'Snails' poems use alliteration (repetition of the same consonants). In
your poem you might like to do the same until you become more confident.
Here are some ideas for shaped poems:

- a football
- a tennis racquet
- glasses
- scissors

- a skeleton
- a snake
- baked beans
- a banana

- a bicycle
- a flower
- a ghost
- a star

- a cricket bat
- a teapot
- a chair
- an umbrella

- a fish
- a TV set
- an eye, ear or nose
- a face

- a motorcar
- curtains
- a worm
- a fly

You can get many more ideas for shaped poems by holding a class brain-storming session. Each student tries to think up a good subject for a shaped poem. Then the teacher writes the subjects on the board. It's quite amazing how one good idea triggers off another!

Here are some more shaped poems which might give you further ideas.

ACROBATS

```
a    a    a    a    a
  c    c    c    c
  r    r    r    r    r
    o    o    o    o
  b    b    b    b    b
    a    a    a    a
  t    t    t    t    t
    s    s    s    s
  t    t    t    t    t
    a    a    a    a
  b    b    b    b    b
    o    o    o    o
  r    r    r    r    r
    c    c    c    c
  a    a    a    a    a
```

IAN HAMILTON FINLAY

THE ANGUISH OF THE MACHINE

THE HEAT IS ON TOO MUCH PRESSURE PACKING UP
THE HEAT IS ON TOO MUCH PRESSURE PACKING UP
THE HEAT IS ON TOO MUCH PRESSURE PACKING UP
THE HEAT IS ON TOO MUCH PRESSURE PACKING UP
THE HEAT IS ON TOO MUCH PRESSURE PACKING UP
THE HEAT IS ON TOO MUCH PRESSURE PACKING UP
THE HEAT IS ON TOO MUCH PRESSURE PACKING UP

CAN'T STAND ANY MORE
CAN'T STAND ANY MORE
CAN'T STAND ANY MORE   STRAIN TOO GREAT
CAN'T STAND ANY MORE   STRAIN TOO GREAT
                              STRAIN TOO GREAT
DON'T HAVE A BREAK-   STRAIN TOO GREAT
DOWN DON'T HAVE A   STRAIN TOO GREAT
BREAK-DOWN DON'T H   STRAIN TOO GREAT
AVE A BREAK-
DOWN   DON'T CRACK UP
                      cool down
                      cool down
                      cool down
         don't   cool down
         lose   cool down
         your   cool down
         nerv   cool down
         e   cool down
         don'
         t
         sto
         pnow

                            don't

                                      stop now

               don't

               don't

PETER MURPHY

FLYING FISH

ALAN RIDDELL

6. The Sea

'Seasonal' means happening only during a certain season of the year. 'Phenomenon' means a remarkable or rare thing or occurrence. After reading through this poem, see whether you can suggest why it is called 'Seasonal Phenomenon'. Keep in mind that the poem has its setting on an American beach, where the swimming season is different from ours.

SEASONAL PHENOMENON

The lifeguard is a man of brawn.
He has a streamlined swim suit on
That fits him like his very skin.
He is not fat, he is not thin;
It is, in fact, his lucky fate
To have no need to watch his weight.
His limbs are trim, his knees unknotted,
His tan is even and unspotted,
He has a profile like Adonis,
And as, with stately, godlike slowness
He regularly paces by,
He wins the soft, admiring eye,
Without half trying to, of each
And every female on the beach.

Oh, let him have his hour of glory —
This creature of a season — for he
Will, as the days grow short, grow sober.
Who cares for lifeguards in October?

RICHARD ARMOUR

Seasonal Phenomenon — Compare the stanzas
(1) What is the poet telling us about the lifeguard in the first stanza?
(2) What happens to the lifeguard in the second stanza?

There is nothing happy or friendly about killing the largest, most harmless living creatures in the world. In fact it is a rather inhuman pursuit, as this poem seeks to show.

KILLING A WHALE

A whale is killed as follows:
A shell is filled with dynamite and
A harpoon takes the shell.
You wait until the great gray back
Breaches the sliding seas, you squint,
Take aim.
The cable snakes like a squirt of paint,
The shell channels deep through fluke
And flank, through mural softness
To bang among the blubber,
Exploding terror through
The hollow fleshy chambers,
While the hooks fly open
Like an umbrella
Gripping the tender tissue.

It dies with some panache,[1]
Whipping the capstan like
A schoolboy's wooden top,
Until the teeth of the machine
Can hold its anger, grip.
Its dead tons thresh for hours
The ravished sea,
Then sink together, sag —
So air is pumped inside
To keep the corpse afloat,
And one of those flags that men
Kill mountains with is stuck
Into this massive death.

Dead whales are rendered down,
Give oil.

DAVID GILL

1 *panache:* display of style; flair

Killing a Whale — Method and message

(1) Re-read the poem and notice the following features that help to make its description and message so real:

   (a) Lines 1–6 read rather like a recipe and this increases the horror of the introduction. Can you say why?

   (b) 'The cable snakes like a squirt of paint' is a vivid simile. See if you can find two other similes in the poem.

   (c) The action of the poem may be divided into five parts. They are:

   lines 1–6   23–28
            7–15   29–30
          16–22

   In your own words, outline what each of these parts contains.

(2) How do you understand the message of this poem? Comment on it.

Pam Ayres now introduces a limpet which offers us some inside information on its lifestyle.

CLAMP THE MIGHTY LIMPET

I am Clamp the Mighty Limpet
I am solid, I am stuck
I am welded to the rockface
With my superhuman suck
I live along the waterline
And in the dreary caves
I am Clamp the Mighty Limpet
I am Ruler of the Waves.

What care I for the shingle,
For the dragging of the tide,
With my unrelenting sucker
And my granite underside?
There's only one reward
For those who come to prise at me
And that's to watch their fingernails
As they go floating out to sea.

Don't upset *me*, I'm a limpet
Though it's plankton I devour
Be very, very careful!
I can move an inch an hour!
Don't you poke or prod me
For I warn you — if you do
You stand there for a fortnight
And I might be stuck on you!

PAM AYRES

Clamp the Mighty Limpet — What does he say?
(1)   What clues tell you that the limpet is very firmly attached to its rock?
(2)   The limpet claims to be the Ruler of the Waves. In what way is this true?
(3)   What is the limpet quite unconcerned about?
(4)   Explain the meaning of 'unrelenting sucker'.
(5)   What happens to those people who prise at the limpet?
(6)   What is the limpet's main food?
(7)   What kind of threat is made in the last stanza?
(8)   Hardly anybody would be worried by this threat. Why?
(9)   What are your feelings about the limpet's lifestyle? Do you feel sorry for it in any way? Why?

THE JELLYFISH

There isn't much a man can do
about a grounded jellyfish
except step over it, or prod
it with his walking stick, and if
he has no walking stick, his shoe.
My feet were bare, so I leaned
to watch the waves relax around
the shiny melted-looking heap.

The jellyfish didn't move,
but then, of course, jellyfishes
don't. They navigate at best
like bottles: When the tide shifts
they bob and drift away. But who
has ever seen a living creature
with a note inside?

I found
an iridescent fish, uneaten
and twitching still, inside the gluey
drying bowel. I saw it jerk,
expand its gills, then quiver, arrested
loosely, loosely and forever.
It shone with pink and green, blue
and yellow, flashed profoundly silver
in each spasm. I knew it was dead
already, and only seemed to work
to free itself.
As I tried to remove
the notion from my mind, the mound
it moved in, like a glassy brain,
was taken from me by a wave
that slid from the ocean without a sound.

WILLIAM PITT ROOT

The Jellyfish — Some questions

(1) Why does the man in the poem feel helpless when he comes across a grounded jellyfish?
(2) What does he end up doing?
(3) What do jellyfish and bottles have in common?
(4) What does the poet find in the jellyfish that is equivalent, in a strange way, to a note in a bottle?
(5) There are plenty of colours mentioned in the third stanza. See whether you can find the one word in the stanza that stands for all of them.
(6) How does the sea help solve the poet's problem?
(7) A simile in the last stanza compares the jellyfish to a ....
(8) 'The sea is mysterious and looks after its own.' Comment on this statement using ideas and examples from the poem where you can.

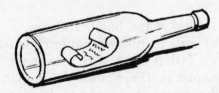

In the poem that follows, two worlds are separated by a pane of glass. In one of them the cold is so terrible that life has almost ceased. In the other there are all the comforting sensations of bustle and life: shouts, the movement of passers-by, and the warmth and leisure of being an interested observer and remembering a past experience.

Yet, a momentary, barely noticeable sign manages to cross from the world of the doomed to the world of the busy living. As you read, ask yourself how you would feel about the . . .

LOBSTERS IN THE WINDOW

First, you think they are dead.
Then you are almost sure
One is beginning to stir.
Out of the crushed ice, slow
As the hands of a schoolroom clock,
He lifts his one great claw
And holds it over his head;
Now, he is trying to walk.

But like a run-down toy;
Like the backward crabs we boys
Splashed after in the creek,
Trapped in jars or a net,
And then took home to keep.
Overgrown, retarded, weak,
He is fumbling yet
From the deep chill of his sleep

As if, in a glacial thaw,
Some ancient thing might wake
Sore and cold and stiff
Struggling to raise one claw
Like a defiant fist;
Yet wavering, as if
Starting to swell and ache
With that thick peg in the wrist.

I should wave back, I guess.
But still in his permanent clench
He's fallen back with the mass
Heaped in their common trench
Who stir, but do not look out
Through the rainstreaming glass,
Hear what the newsboys shout,
Or see the raincoats pass.

W. D. SNODGRASS

THE SHARK

He seemed to know the harbour,
So leisurely he swam;
His fin,
Like a piece of sheet-iron,
Three-cornered,
And with knife-edge,
Stirred not a bubble
As it moved
With its base-line on the water.

His body was tubular
And tapered
And smoke-blue,
And as he passed the wharf
He turned,
And snapped at a flat-fish
That was dead and floating.
And I saw the flash of a white throat,
And a double row of white teeth,
And eyes of metallic grey,
Hard and narrow and slit.

Then out of the harbour,
With that three-cornered fin,
Shearing without a bubble the water
Lithely,
Leisurely,
He swam —
That strange fish,
Tubular, tapered, smoke-blue,
Part vulture, part wolf,
Part neither — for his blood was cold.

E. J. PRATT

The Shark — Studying the description

(1) What gave the poet the impression that the shark knew the harbour?

(2) 'His fin, Like a piece of sheet-iron . . .' What is this comparison called? Why is the shark's fin like a piece of sheet-iron?

(3) The poet repeats the words 'tubular' and 'tapered'. What pictures do these words give you of the shark?

(4)   The poet repeats 'smoke-blue' and 'white'. What feelings do these colours convey in the context?

(5)   What are the four adjectives used to describe the shark's eyes. What do these words suggest about the shark's temperament?

(6)   Can you suggest why the shark is 'part vulture'?

(7)   Why is the shark 'part wolf'?

(8)   Each of the three stanzas describes a different stage of the shark's progress through the harbour. What are the three stages?

(9)   Briefly list the qualities of the shark described by the poet.

(10)   Did you enjoy this poem? Why?

And here's another shark — is he any different? This time a single feature of the shark is stressed: his 'long dark thought'. What *is* the shark's single long dark thought? Why will it never be completed? How about his manners? Try to discover the answers to these questions as you read.

THE SHARK

My sweet, let me tell you about the Shark.
Though his eyes are bright, his thought is dark.
He's quiet — that speaks well of him.
So does the fact that he can swim.
But though he swims without a sound,
Wherever he swims he looks around
With those two bright eyes and that one dark thought.
He has only one but he thinks it a lot.
And the thought he thinks but can never complete
Is his long dark thought of something to eat.
Most anything does. And I have to add
That when he eats, his manners are bad.
He's a gulper, a ripper, a snatcher, a grabber.
Yes, his manners are drab. But his thought is drabber.
That one dark thought he can never complete
Of something — anything — somehow to eat.

Be careful where you swim, my sweet.

JOHN CIARDI

7. Rhyme and Limerick

Rhyme

Probably the simplest rhymes of all are those to be found in 'nursery rhymes', followed closely by those used in limericks. Look at the limerick below. The words in heavy type rhyme with each other, as do the words in italics. Keep in mind that rhyme depends on sound, not on spelling.

There was an old person of **Crewe**
Who found a dead mouse in his **stew.**
Said the waiter : 'Don't *shout*
And wave it *about*,
Or the rest will be wanting one **too**!'

Rhyming pairs

In this list of twenty-four words, there are twelve pairs of rhyming words. Rearrange them in rhyming couples.

tough	toe	enough	bread
dough	here	should	made
stood	plight	mare	pearl
pair	dear	through	die
blue	spite	said	fly
weighed	smile	aisle	twirl

Find rhyming words
Write down words that rhyme with:

spear	past	rusty	sweet	throne	pinch
young	tall	stone	snow	joke	fate
told	taught	house	corn	lace	four
sound	roaring	fruit	white	people	bump
lying	seeing	showers	crow	town	hand

Limericks

Read through the following limericks and notice the rhyming pattern common to them all.

A wonderful bird is the pelican,
His beak can hold more than his belican.
He can take in his beak,
Enough food for a week —
I'm blowed if I know how the helican.

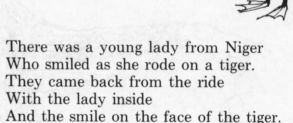

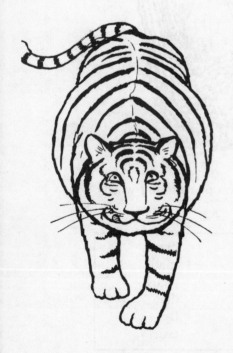

There was a young lady from Niger
Who smiled as she rode on a tiger.
They came back from the ride
With the lady inside
And the smile on the face of the tiger.

There was a young man of Bengal
Who went to a fancy-dress ball.
He went just for fun,
Dressed up as a bun,
And a dog ate him up in the hall.

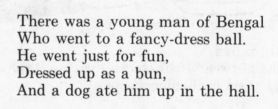

A tone-deaf old person from Tring,
When somebody asked him to sing,
Replied, 'It is odd
But I cannot tell "God
Save the weasel" from "Pop goes the King".'

There was an old fellow of Lyme
Who married three wives at a time.
When asked: 'Why the third?'
He replied 'One's absurd —
And bigamy, sir, is a crime!'

There was a fat lady of Clyde
Whose shoelaces once came untied.
She feared that to bend
Would display her rear end,
So she cried and she cried and she cried.

There was a young girl of Asturias
Whose temper was frantic and furious.
She used to throw eggs
At her grandmother's legs —
A habit unpleasant, but curious.

The bottle of perfume that Willie sent
Was highly displeasing to Millicent.
Her thanks were so cold
That they quarrelled, I'm told,
Through that silly scent Willie sent Millicent.

There once was a sculptor of mark
Whom they chose to brighten Hyde Park.
Some thought his design
Most markedly fine —
But more liked it best in the dark.

A sea-serpent saw a big tanker,
Bit a hole in her side and then sank her.
It swallowed the crew
In a minute or two,
And then picked its teeth with the anchor.

There was a young lady of Lynn
Who was so excessively thin
That when she essayed
To drink lemonade
She slipped through the straw and fell in.

There was a young lady named Bright
Who travelled much faster than light.
She started one day
In the relative way
And returned on the previous night.

Limerick form

You will have noticed from these limericks that there is a standard, predict-able form or pattern that each limerick obeys:

(a)   it has five lines;
(b)   the first, second and fifth lines have one rhyme and the third and fourth lines have a different rhyme;
(c)   the rhythm and number of syllables in lines 1, 2 and 5 match, while the rhythm and number of syllables in lines 3 and 4 also match;
(d)   lines 3 and 4 are short lines.

Because a limerick is never very serious, the last line is usually very import-ant. It is the 'punchline' of the limerick — the line on which the humour of the limerick hinges.

Your turn

(1)   Make a list of as many words as you can that rhyme with the following place-names. Half-rhymes and other 'forced' rhymes may be included (e.g. Sydney — didn't he).

Perth	Kent	Ryde	Parkes	York
St Kilda	Broome	Mars	Calcutta	Hay

(2)   Choose two of the places above and write your own limericks. If you like, use some of the rhyme-words you have already worked out.
(3)   Try to make up limericks of your own using these first lines:
   (a)   There was a young lady from Surrey
   (b)   A very old man from Tring
   (c)   When running along the street to school
   (d)   A foolish young man named Joe
   (e)   A little old lady from Zee

(4)   Write two limericks using some of the following rhyming words. You
       may choose any three and use them in any order.
       (a)   Hobart/slow start/Mozart/go-kart
       (b)   Grong Grong/ping-pong/ning-nong/King Kong
       (c)   ACT/bee/key/cup of tea/recipe
       (d)   Mt Isa/wiser/despise 'er/geyser/miser
       (e)   Collingwood/eating pud[ding]/being good

Playing with Words

Many short humorous poems derive their humour from the fact that the
poet is 'playing with words'. He may have made up new words; he may have
'forced' some of his rhymes; or he may have simply used a normal word
in an unusual way. Read through the following humorous verses, all by
anonymous poets.

HOW THE THIEF THOVE

Forth from his den to steal he stole,
His bags full of clink he clunk;
And many a wicked smile he smole,
And many a wink he wunk.

Thump 'n' shake
The plum-sauce bottle;
None'll come
And then a lot'll.

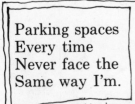

Parking spaces
Every time
Never face the
Same way I'm.

ODE TO A SNEEZE

I sneezed a sneeze into the air,
It fell to earth I know not where;
But hard and froze were the looks of those
In whose vicinity I snoze.

Forth went the thunder-god
Riding on his filly.
'I'm Thor,' he cried.
His horse replied:
'You forgot your thaddle, thilly.'

Your turn

(1) Look at the following lines:

> 'The little mouse lived with the mice;
> He built his house among their hice.'

The rhyme is made by creating a regular, but incorrect, plural. Use this kind of approach to write two rhyming lines of your own on each of the following:

(a)	ox/oxen	box/
(b)	goose/geese	moose/
(c)	brother/brethren	mother/
(d)	man/men	can/

(2) Write five short rhyming verses, using each of the five contractions below as one of the rhymes. Note the example:

> Packed for holidays.
> Off we drive.
> Who's forgotten something?
> I've!

(a) Can't
(b) We're
(c) We've
(d) They'd
(e) Isn't

8. City Life

For a commuter (a person who travels to and from the city to work) the pace of life is likely to be fast but jerky — happening after happening, and each one different.

The way 'City Life' is written reflects this brisk, jerky pace. Be sensitive to this aspect of the poem as you read through it.

CITY LIFE

City wakes. Sun comes up
Hurried breakfast. Feed the pup
Workers wake. Children dream
Tea or coffee? Milk or cream?

Say Good Morning. Say Good-bye
Quickly leave. Babies cry
Where's the train? Why the fuss?
Never mind, catch a bus

Grab a seat. Down the hill
Women standing. Looks can kill!
Read the paper. Have a smoke
Ignore the cough. Enjoy the joke

Cross the road. Mind the tram
Silly women. Watch that pram!
In the lift. Morning, Jock
Just in time. Beat the clock

Start some work. Have some coffee
File some papers. Chew some toffee
Sign a cheque. Draw a plan
Build a house. Drive a van

Grab a sandwich. That's your lunch
Where's that file? Got a hunch
See the boss. Hope it's short
Might have known. Where's that report?

Grab those plans. Feeling ill
Just my luck. Ink would spill!
Where's my watch? Ten to four
Another letter. Maybe more

Off at last. First one through
Forgot my hat. Join the queue
Grab a taxi. Hurry past
Won't get booked for driving fast.

Have some tea. Take my pills
Read the mail. Only bills
Have a beer. Watch the news
Take a shower. Clean my shoes.

Read a book. Watch a show
Off to bed. Where else to go?
Through the window, starlight peeps
I'm awake. The city sleeps.

Adapted from 'City Life'
JOHN CARDIFF

City Life — Topics and phrases

Look at the table of topics that follows. From the poem, extract one phrase
for each of the topics — a phrase that enlarges on the topic in each case.
The first one has been done to give you the idea.

Topic	Phrase	Topic	Phrase
DAWN	'Sun comes up'	SNACKS	
BREAKFAST		ACCIDENT	
PET		MEDICINE	
BUS		RELAX	
WALKING		TV	
PUNCTUALITY		LIGHTS OUT	

A tournament (old word: *tourney*) was a military sport of the Middle Ages in which knights engaged in combat, mainly on horseback, with spear or sword.

CENTRAL PARK TOURNEY

Cars
In the Park
With long spear lights
Ride at each other
Like armoured knights;
Rush,
Miss the mark,
Pierce the dark,
Dash by!
Another two
Try.

Staged
In the Park
From dusk
To dawn,
The tourney goes on:
Rush,
Miss the mark,
Pierce the dark,
Dash by!
Another two
Try.

MILDRED WESTON

Central Park Tourney — Looking into the poem
(1) What is being compared to Medieval knights at a tournament?
(2) Where is the arena for this modern tournament?
(3) Why is the tourney only from dusk to dawn?
(4) 'With long spear lights ...' What exactly is meant by this?
(5) Which words in the poem suggest rapid movement?
(6) In both stanzas, the last six lines are the same. What are they describing?
(7) What would it be called, in modern times, if the two combatants did *not* miss the mark?
(8) Why are short, sharp lines appropriate for this poem?

Who but Pam Ayres would write with such feeling, sympathy and gentle humour about a battered mascot wired to the front of a garbage truck?

Notice, as you read through the poem, how certain features of the dolly's appearance — her dress, her rosy cheeks, her squeaker — are shown in their present wretched state and compared with their past state of freshness and charm. In her past life she was happy, until she was replaced ... by what? Why?

As you read, find the lines that amuse you most, and then try to put your finger on the reason for the popularity of Pam Ayres's poetry.

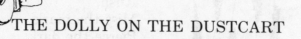

THE DOLLY ON THE DUSTCART

I'm the dolly on the dustcart,
I can see you're not impressed,
I'm fixed above the driver's cab,
With wire across me chest,
The dustman see, he spotted me,
Going in the grinder,
And he fixed me on the lorry,
I dunno if that was kinder.

This used to be a lovely dress,
In pink and pretty shades,
But it's torn now, being on the cart,
And black as the ace of spades,
There's dirt all round me face,
And all across me rosy cheeks,
Well, I've had me head thrown back,
But we ain't had no rain for weeks.

I used to be a 'Mama' doll,
Tipped forward, I'd say 'Mum',
But the rain got in me squeaker,
And now I been struck dumb,
I had two lovely blue eyes,
But out in the wind and weather,
One's sunk back in me head like,
And one's gone altogether.

I'm not a soft, flesh coloured dolly
Modern children like so much,
I'm one of those hard old dollies,
What are very cold to touch,
Modern dolly's underwear
Leaves me a bit nonplussed,
I haven't got a bra,
But then I haven't got a bust!

Yet I was happy in that doll's house,
I was happy as a Queen,
I never knew that Tiny Tears
Was coming on the scene,
I heard of dolls with hair that grew,
And I was quite enthralled,
Until I realised *my* head
Was hard and pink ... and bald.

So I travels with the rubbish,
Out of fashion, out of style,
Out of me environment,
For mile after mile,
No longer prized ... dustbinized!
Unfeminine, Untidy,
I'm the dolly on the dustcart.
There'll be no collection Friday.

PAM AYRES

A madrigal is a type of song, usually about love. As you read the next poem think about the things Mokie hates, and the things he loves. Who, according to Mokie, leads the ideal way of life?

MOKIE'S MADRIGAL

Some little boys get shushed all day,
Can't make noises when they play;
All they do is just annoy —
I want to be a paper-boy;
Paper-boys can ride and ride
Free on all the trams outside,
No-one shushes when they sing,
They can shout like anything:
   Sunnamirra, murdafiar!
   Pyar, pyar! Wannapyar?
   Tirra lirra, tirra lirra!
   Murdafiar, Sunnamirra!

Some little boys can never get
All the ice-creams they could eat;
Paper-boys don't ask their Mums,
They've got bags of treys and brums;
When a paper-boy is full,
He goes and buys a bicycle —
Poppa, Poppa, let me out
To be a paper-boy, and shout:
   Sunnamirra, murdafiar!
   Pyar, pyar! Wannapyar?
   Tirra lirra, tirra lirra!
   Murdafiar, Sunnamirra!

Some little boys can never go
Everywhere they're wanting to;
Paper-boys can choose their track,
Hop on their bikes, and not come back —
Poppa, Poppa, can't you see
How you can get rid of me?
No more Mokie, no more noise,
Only other paper-boys'
    Sunnamirra, murdafiar!
    Pyar, pyar! Wannapyar?
    Tirra lirra, tirra lirra!
    Murdafiar, Sunnamirra!

RONALD MCCUAIG

Mokie's Madrigal — Over to you

(1) What are some of the things that Mokie can't do? In what ways do paper-boys have more freedom than Mokie?

(2) Which lines of the poem most remind you of the lyrics of a song?

(3) From this box of feelings, choose those that apply to Mokie, and explain why.

envy
happiness
discontent
alarm
admiration

(4) The words of the 'chorus' are meant to be those actually used by a newsboy as he shouts in his strange paper-seller's language to passers-by. Read the chorus out loud, then write down what you think the words mean in clear English.

(5) What offer does Mokie make to his father at the end of the poem? Do you think his father will think it tempting? Why?

STREET SCENE

A helicopter in the sky
  Observed the traffic down below,
Establishing the where and why
  Of anything that stopped the flow.

A motorist in a crawling queue,
  Distracted by the whirring rotor,
Looked up to get a better view
  And rammed (of course) another motor.

Policemen worked for half the day
  To clear things, and at last succeeded.
The helicopter whirled away
  To see where else it might be needed.

                                    PETER SUFFOLK

Street Scene – Reporting the accident

Now zoom down for a closer look at the scene with this exercise. File a report
on the accident outlined in the poem.

```
ACCIDENT REPORT

TYPE OF ACCIDENT: ...........................................................................
NO. OF CARS INVOLVED: .............................
STATEMENT BY HELICOPTER PILOT ON DUTY: ...........................................
...................................................................................................
STATEMENT BY MOTORIST:
(signed in hospital) .........................................................................
...................................................................................................
...................................................................................................
STATEMENT BY POLICE: ...................................................................
...................................................................................................
...................................................................................................
...................................................................................................
BLAME FOR ACCIDENT:
(final summing up) ..........................................................................
...................................................................................................
...................................................................................................
```

Final thoughts

There is a lesson to be learnt from the events described in 'Street Scene'. What, in your opinion, is this lesson? Does it apply to life in general and not just to this situation? How?

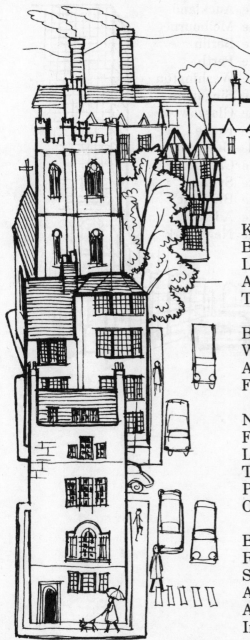

I LIKE THE TOWN

Kids are supposed to like the country—
Because it is natural,
Like them.
And is made up of villages, small
Things, like them.

But I like the town,
With proper white faces
And no empty spaces
Filled with queer noises.

Not the big city,
For that's a pity!
Longwinded like London,
Tottery like Tokyo,
Panting like Paris,
Or choked like Chicago.

But a middling-sized town,
Roads going up,
Streets going down,
And people you know
And people you don't.
In short, just so.

D. J. ENRIGHT

I Like the Town — A question and an activity

(1)   Give the reasons why kids are supposed to like the country.
(2)   Note how four big cities are described in the poem. Supply, from your imagination, an appropriate adjective for each of the following cities.

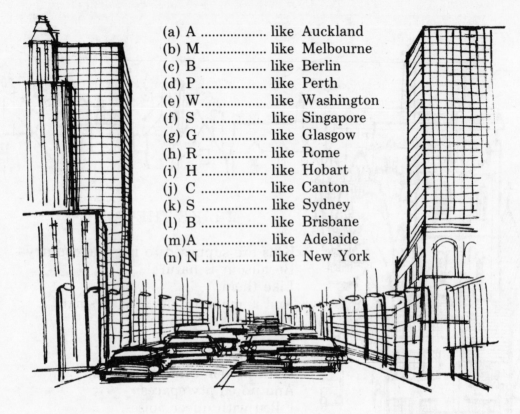

(a) A .... like Auckland
(b) M................. like Melbourne
(c) B .... like Berlin
(d) P .... like Perth
(e) W................. like Washington
(f) S .... like Singapore
(g) G .... like Glasgow
(h) R .... like Rome
(i) H .... like Hobart
(j) C .... like Canton
(k) S .... like Sydney
(l) B .... like Brisbane
(m)A .... like Adelaide
(n) N .... like New York

9. Writing Your First Poems

This unit is designed to give students confidence to start writing poetry of their own. Each section is so structured that all students in the class will have little difficulty in making up poems of their own.

Blackboard Poetry

Read 'Wish Poem' through.

WISH POEM

I wish my father would fall downstairs and break his head;
I wish I had teeth like fingernails;
I wish my fingernails were hard as diamonds;
I wish my sister would explode;
I wish I had a house of my own, my most prized trophy my mother's head;
I wish my other sister would grow thin as a match so I could lose her down a crack;
I wish I had purple ears with yellow spots.

ANONYMOUS

A class 'Wish Poem'

Now the teacher or a student writes up on the board a number of times, 'I wish ...' Then members of the class take turns completing the lines with wishes of their own.

Read the following poem, 'I Saw a Fish-pond All on Fire'.

I SAW A FISH-POND ALL ON FIRE

I saw a fish-pond all on fire,
I saw a house bow to a squire,
I saw a person twelve feet high,
I saw a cottage in the sky,
I saw a balloon made of lead,
I saw a coffin drop down dead,
I saw two sparrows run a race,
I saw two horses making lace,
I saw a girl just like a cat,
I saw a kitten wear a hat,
I saw a man who saw these too,
And said though strange they all were true.

ANONYMOUS

A class 'I Saw . . .' poem

The teacher or a student writes up on the board a number of times, 'I saw . . .' Then members of the class take turns completing the lines with descriptions of their own. This time, as in 'I Saw a Fish-pond All on Fire', each pair of lines must rhyme.

More Poems to Complete

Poems of the senses

Make up poems of your own by completing each of the lines.

I see .... (e.g. a golden sunset)
I hear ....
I feel ....
I smell ....
I taste ....

'Hello/Goodbye' poems

Try some 'Hello/Goodbye' poems. They're very easy.

Hello holidays, goodbye school.
Hellow lollies, goodbye teeth.
Hello ...., goodbye ....
Hello ...., goodbye ....
Hello ...., goodbye ....
Hello ...., goodbye ....
Hello ...., goodbye ....
Hello ...., goodbye ....

'Is' poems

Try a few 'Is' poems. The first line of one of the following 'Is' poems has been completed to give you the idea.

Summer is air-conditioning units whirring.
Winter is ....
.... is ....
.... is ....
.... is ....
.... is ....
.... is ....

School is ....
A teacher is ....
Homework is ....
Sport is ....
English is ....
My friend is ....
Friday is ....

'Are' poems
Now, using the same technique, make up some 'Are' poems.

> Cats are bundles of fur.
> Cars are ....
> .... are ....
> .... are ....
> .... are ....
> .... are ....

Colours in poetry
Try your hand at writing a colour poem.

> Red is ....
> Green is ....
> White is ....
> Purple is ....
> Pink is ....
> Grey is ....

Adverb poems that rhyme
Students can have a lot of fun making up adverb poems. It's so easy. First of all you need to choose an adverb. Adverbs mostly end in 'ly' — e.g. angrily, silently, sweetly, slowly, greedily, awkwardly, etc. Having chosen your adverb, you make it the first word of each line of your poem. Then collect pairs of rhyming words and let your imagination do the rest. Here's what one student wrote.

SLOWLY

> Slowly snails make their trail;
> Slowly old people grow frail;
> Slowly the sun sets in the west;
> Slowly a boy does a maths test;
>
> Slowly a child learns to walk;
> Slowly the hunter aims at the hawk;
> Slowly the diver rises from the deep;
> Slowly I prepare for sleep.

'Have You Ever Seen a . . .?' poems

Read through these three 'Have you ever seen a . . .?' poems, written by students. Then try to write some of your own. Be sure to use plenty of hyphenated words and words ending in '-ed' and '-ing'.

Have you ever seen a tennis player?
Racquet-wielding, sweat-drenched, angry-faced, defeated.

Have you ever seen a fish?
Zig-zagging, shiny-scaled, stream-lined.

Have you ever seen a gorilla?
Pop-eyed, big-mouthed, long-tailed, fat chubby-bellied.

Haiku

A pleasant way of writing your own poetry is to imitate the structure of the Japanese *haiku*. The haiku is a simple but subtle little poem of seventeen syllables. It has three short lines of five, seven, and five syllables respectively. The five haiku that follow have been translated from Japanese into English.

BRAND-NEW KITE

In unending rain
The house-pent boy is fretting
With his brand-new kite.

HAIKU

A bitter morning:
Sparrows sitting together
Without any necks.

THE MOON ON THE WATER

Though it be broken —
Broken again — still it's there:
The moon on the water.

AUTUMN

Now the old scarecrow
Looks just like other people . . .
Drenching Autumn rain.

FULL MOON

Bright the full moon shines:
On the matting of the floor,
Shadows of the pines.

Copy the pattern of these haiku and create simple picture-poems of
your own. (See if you can express special moods, feelings or ideas, as
in the examples. The 'meaning' of Japanese haiku is often to be found
'beneath the surface' of the description.)

10. Rhythm

Rhythm is the swing or the beat that can run so effectively through lines of poetry. Read through John Masefield's poem, 'Cargoes'.

CARGOES

Quinquireme of Nineveh from distant Ophir,
Rowing home to haven in sunny Palestine,
With a cargo of ivory,
And apes and peacocks,
Sandalwood, cedarwood, and sweet white wine.

Stately Spanish galleon coming from the Isthmus,
Dipping through the Tropics by the palm-green shores,
With a cargo of diamonds,
Emeralds, amethysts,
Topazes, and cinnamon, and gold moidores.

Dirty British coaster with a salt-caked smoke stack,
Butting through the Channel in the mad March days,
With a cargo of Tyne coal,
Road-rails, pig-lead,
Firewood, iron-ware, and cheap tin trays.

JOHN MASEFIELD

Cargoes — For you to think about
(1) A quinquireme was, in Roman times, a ship with five banks of oars. With this clue in mind, what is the rhythm of the first stanza of the poem?
(2) To what is the rhythm of the second stanza similar?
(3) What is being described in the third stanza? Is the rhythm faster than in the other two stanzas? Why? What does the beat or rhythm resemble?

Here is a poem about a fence.

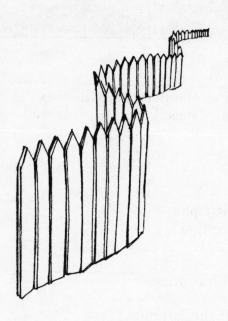

THE PICKETY FENCE

The pickety fence,
The pickety fence,
Give it a lick it's
The pickety fence
Give it a lick it's
The clickety fence
Give it a lick it's
A lickety fence
Give it a lick
Give it a lick
Give it a lick
With a rickety stick
Pickety
Pickety
Pickety
Pick.

DAVID MCCORD

The Pickety Fence — What did you hear?

It seems strange to think that a fence can have rhythm, but if you read the poem to yourself you'll be quite aware of it. Can you identify the rhythm? What is it?

Identifying the rhythm or movement

Look at the lines of poetry below. Read them to yourself, savour the rhythms, then try to identify the particular rhythm or movement used in each.

(1)   This is the night mail crossing the border,
      Bringing the cheque and the postal order,
      Letters for the rich, letters for the poor,
      The shop at the corner and the girl next door.

(2)   Click go the shears boys, click, click, click;
      Wide is his blow and his hands move quick;
      The ringer looks round and is beaten by a blow,
      And curses the old snagger with the bare-bellied yeo.

(3)   Half a league, half a league,
Half a league onward,
All in the valley of Death
Rode the six hundred.

Here is a famous love-story full of romance, adventure — and tragedy.

THE HIGHWAYMAN

Part One

The wind was a torrent of darkness among the gusty trees,
The moon was a ghostly galleon tossed upon cloudy seas,
The road was a ribbon of moonlight over the purple moor,
And the highwayman came riding —
   Riding — riding —
The highwayman came riding, up to the old inn-door.

He'd a French cocked-hat on his forehead, a bunch of lace at his
  chin,
A coat of the claret velvet, and breeches of brown doe-skin;
They fitted with never a wrinkle: his boots were up to the thigh!
And he rode with a jewelled twinkle,
  His pistol butts a-twinkle,
His rapier hilt a-twinkle, under the jewelled sky.

Over the cobbles he clattered and clashed in the dark inn-yard,
And he tapped with his whip on the shutters, but all was locked and
   barred;
He whistled a tune to the window, and who should be waiting there
But the landlord's black-eyed daughter,
  Bess, the landlord's daughter,
Plaiting a dark red love-knot into her long black hair.

And dark in the dark old inn-yard a stable-wicket creaked
Where Tim the ostler listened; his face was white and peaked;
His eyes were hollows of madness, his hair like mouldy hay,
But he loved the landlord's daughter,
  The landlord's red-lipped daughter.
Dumb as a dog he listened, and he heard the robber say —

'One kiss, my bonny sweetheart, I'm after a prize to-night,
But I shall be back with the yellow gold before the morning light;
Yet, if they press me sharply, and harry me through the day,
Then look for me by moonlight,
   Watch for me by moonlight,
I'll come to thee by moonlight, though hell should bar the way.'

He rose upright in the stirrups; he scarce could reach her hand,
But she loosened her hair i' the casement! His face burned like a
   brand
As the black cascade of perfume came tumbling over his breast;
And he kissed its waves in the moonlight,
  (Oh, sweet black waves in the moonlight!)
Then he tugged at his rein in the moonlight, and galloped away to
   the West.

Part Two

He did not come in the dawning; he did not come at noon;
And out o' the tawny sunset, before the rise o' the moon,
When the road was a gipsy's ribbon, looping the purple moor,
A red-coat troop came marching —
   Marching — Marching —
King George's men came marching, up to the old inn-door.

They said no word to the landlord, they drank his ale instead,
But they gagged his daughter and bound her to the foot of her narrow
   bed;
Two of them knelt at her casement, with muskets at their side!
There was death at every window;
   And hell at one dark window;
For Bess could see, through her casement, the road that *he* would
   ride.

They had tied her up to attention, with many a sniggering jest;
They had bound a musket beside her, with the muzzle beneath her
   breast!
'Now keep good watch!' and they kissed her.
She heard the dead man say —
'Look for me by moonlight;
   Watch for me by moonlight;
I'll come to thee by moonlight, though hell should bar the way!'

She twisted her hands behind her; but all the knots held good!
She writhed her hands till her fingers were wet with sweat or blood!
They stretched and strained in the darkness, and the hours crawled
    by like years,
Till, now, on the stroke of midnight,
  Cold, on the stroke of midnight,
The tip of one finger touched it! The trigger at least was hers!

The tip of one finger touched it; she strove no more for the rest!
Up, she stood up to attention, with the muzzle beneath her breast,
She would not risk their hearing; she would not strive again;
For the road lay bare in the moonlight;
  Blank and bare in the moonlight;
And the blood of her veins in the moonlight throbbed to her love's
    refrain.

Tlot-tlot, tlot-tlot! Had they heard it? The horse-hoofs ringing clear;
Tlot-tlot, tlot-tlot, in the distance? Were they deaf that they did not
    hear?
Down the ribbon of moonlight, over the brow of the hill,
The highwayman came riding,
  Riding, riding!
The red-coats looked to their priming! She stood up straight and
    still!

Tlot-tlot, in the frosty silence! *Tlot-tlot,* in the echoing night!
Nearer he came and nearer! Her face was like a light!
Her eyes grew wide for a moment; she drew one last deep breath,
Then her finger moved in the moonlight,
  Her musket shattered the moonlight,
Shattered her breast in the moonlight and warned him — with her
    death.

He turned; he spurred to the Westward; he did not know who stood
Bowed, with her head o'er the musket, drenched with her own red
    blood!
Not till the dawn he heard it, and his face grew grey to hear
How Bess, the landlord's daughter,
  The landlord's black-eyed daughter,
Had watched for her love in the moonlight, and died in the darkness
    there.

Back, he spurred like a madman, shrieking a curse to the sky,
With the white road smoking behind him and his rapier brandished
   high!
Blood-red were his spurs i' the golden noon; wine-red was his velvet
   coat;
When they shot him down on the highway,
   Down like a dog on the highway,
And he lay in his blood on the highway, with the bunch of lace at
   his throat.

.   .   .   .   .

And still of a winter's night, they say, when the wind is in the trees,
When the moon is a ghostly galleon tossed upon cloudy seas,
When the road is a ribbon of moonlight over the purple moor,
A highwayman comes riding —
   Riding — riding —
A highwayman comes riding, up to the old inn-door.

Over the cobbles he clatters and clangs in the dark inn-yard;
And he taps with his whip on the shutters, but all is locked and
   barred;
He whistles a tune to the window, and who should be waiting there
But the landlord's black-eyed daughter,
   Bess, the landlord's daughter,
Plaiting a dark red love-knot into her long black hair.

ALFRED NOYES

The Highwayman — Closer scrutiny

(1)   What words convey the movement of the wind?
(2)   What words suggest the rhythm of the highwayman on horseback as
      he approaches the inn?
(3)   'The moon was a ghostly galleon' and 'The road was a ribbon of moon-
      light' are both metaphors. What picture do these metaphors bring to
      your mind?
(4)   In the poem we are told how the highwayman was dressed. What do
      you learn about his character from this description?
(5)   'Over the cobbles he clattered and clashed ...' What words here
      suggest the actual sounds that the highwayman and his horse were
      making?

(6)   'His hair like mouldy hay' and 'Dumb as a dog he listened' are both examples of what figure of speech?

(7)   What firm promise did the highwayman make to Bess?

(8)   Who betrayed the highwayman to the soldiers? Why? Give evidence from the poem.

(9)   'There was death at every window' and 'hell at one dark window'. Why was there hell at one window in particular?

(10)   'She heard the dead man say ...' Why 'the dead man'?

(11)   By midnight, what had Bess managed to do?

(12)   How did Bess warn her highwayman?

(13)   How did the highwayman react?

(14)   When he heard, at dawn, the news of Bess's sacrifice, what change came over him?

(15)   'Back, he spurred ... brandished high!' There's a fast and furious rhythm in these lines. Can you explain why?

(16)   The last word on the highwayman and Bess is spoken in the two stanzas following the five dots. These stanzas are printed in italics. In your own words, explain what is different about them.

(17)   What comments would you make about the love of Bess and the highwayman?

11. Strange Happenings

THE LESSON

Chaos ruled OK in the classroom
as bravely the teacher walked in
the havocwreakers ignored him
his voice was lost in the din

'The theme for today is violence
and homework will be set
I'm going to teach you a lesson
one that you'll never forget'

He picked on a boy who was shouting
and throttled him then and there
then garrotted the girl behind him
(the one with grotty hair)

Then sword in hand he hacked his way
between the chattering rows
'First come, first severed' he declared
'fingers, feet, or toes'

He threw the sword at a latecomer
it struck with deadly aim
then pulling out a shotgun
he continued with his game

The first blast cleared the backrow
(where those who skive hang out)
they collapsed like rubber dinghies
when the plug's pulled out

'Please may I leave the room sir?'
a trembling vandal enquired
'Of course you may' said teacher
put the gun to his temple and fired

The Head popped a head round the doorway
to see why a din was being made
nodded understandingly
then tossed in a grenade

And when the ammo was well spent
with blood on every chair
Silence shuffled forward
with its hands up in the air

The teacher surveyed the carnage
the dying and the dead
He waggled a finger severely
'Now let that be a lesson' he said

ROGER MCGOUGH

The Lesson — Concentrating on the poem

(1)   In the poem there are many examples of extreme violence. Write down a few of them.

(2)   The events in the poem are too incredible to be believed. Do you agree? Explain your viewpoint.

(3)   What are your feelings towards the teacher in the poem?

(4)   What is a vandal? Why was the vandal trembling?

(5)   The poem is arranged in stanzas of four lines. Write down the stanza you liked (a) best, and (b) least, and explain why.

(6)   Draw a picture showing what happens in one or two of the stanzas.

(7)   *Corporal* punishment is different from *capital* punishment. Try to explain the difference.

(8)   Explain the meanings of (a) throttled, (b) havocwreakers, (c) severed, (d) hacked.

(9)   The teacher said: 'I'm going to teach you a lesson
           one that you'll never forget'
Do you think he was successful? Why?

(10)   'The Lesson' is a very violent poem. Did you enjoy it? Why? What kind of poetry do you like? (Happy, or serious, or 'weird', or what?) Why?

What do you think?

(1) This poem is written from a teacher's viewpoint. What about the students' viewpoint? What do you think would happen if the students took over your school?

(2) Have you ever been in a classroom where there was chaos (extreme disorder)? Describe what happened.

(3) When there is a lot of noise in the classroom between lessons, and your teacher arrives, what happens?

(4) In your own life you probably will have witnessed violence of some kind. Briefly describe the experience in two or three sentences. Then read your description aloud to the class and compare it with the experiences of your friends.

(5) Some people think that our society is becoming more and more violent. Do you agree? Why?

(6) Do you believe that teachers have to punish students? Why? What are some of the punishments you dislike?

(7) Do you think that some of your teachers have a lot to put up with? Why?

This poem was written in the days of pounds, shillings and pence, before we changed to dollars and cents. Let's hope that Miss Strawberry's purse has not changed over to decimal currency.

MISS STRAWBERRY'S PURSE

Miss Strawberry has a long fat purse
To keep her money in.
It is a rare and handsome purse
Made of crocodile skin.
It is a crocodile skin without a doubt
For she did not take the crocodile out
And when she walks to town to shop
He follows behind her clop, clop-clop,
And opens his mouth and bellows aloud
And swishes his tail amongst the crowd.
Now and again there's an angry mutter
As a man is swept into the gutter.
When in a shop it is time to pay
Shopkeepers look at the brute in dismay
When Miss Strawberry says 'Crocky, open wide,'

And 'Shopman, if you can dodge his paws
And reach beyond those ugly jaws,
You'll find your money deep inside —
But I warn you if you make him cough
He'll probably bite your arm right off.'
The shopkeeper usually says 'No worry.
Pay next month. I'm in no hurry.'
But a grocer once, owed four-pounds-ten,
Said 'That's worth more than one of my men.'
He called his errand-boy, 'Hey, son,
Come over here, we'll have some fun,
I'll hold your legs and guard you while
You crawl in this quiet old crocodile
And collect in his vitals four-pounds-ten.
If you bring it out again
I'll give you sixpence for your trouble.
Come here, son, and at the double!'
Now the length of Miss Strawberry's crocodile's throat
Is four times as long as a shopman's coat.
The crocodile opened fearfully wide
And the errand-boy crawled right down inside.
When he had gathered four-pounds-ten
And hurriedly tried to back out again,
The crocodile closed his jaws with a smile,
Saying, 'One of the joys of a crocodile,
Indeed you might say, his favourite joy,
Is making a meal of a messenger-boy.'

ERIC C. ROLLS

Poet's Corner

Eric C. Rolls has explained his inspiration for 'Miss Strawberry's Purse':
'One day Kerry Jane, my daughter, who was walking about the verandah
in a strange manner, said "I wish she'd bring back my head. I can't
see where I'm going," and Kim her brother, who was hopping on one
foot, said "She's an awful old woman, isn't she? She's got my foot, too."
When I said "Who has?" they answered together "Miss Strawberry".'
The poet then went away, and within a few months he had written a
whole book of Miss Strawberry poems.

GEORGE AND THE DRAGONFLY

Georgie Jennings was spit almighty.
When the golly was good
he could down a dragonfly at 30 feet
and drown a 100 midges with the fallout.
At the drop of a cap
he would outspit lads
years older and twice his size.
Freckled and rather frail
he assumed the quiet dignity
beloved of schoolboy heroes.

But though a legend in his own playtime
Georgie Jennings failed miserably in the classroom
and left school at 15 to work for his father.
And talents such as spitting
are considered unbefitting
for upandcoming porkbutchers.

I haven't seen him since,
but like to imagine some summer soiree
when, after a day moistening mince,
George and his wife entertain tanned friends.
And after dinner, sherrytongued talk
drifts back to schooldays
the faces halfrecalled, the adventures
overexaggerated. And the next thing
that shy sharpshooter of days gone by
is led, vainly protesting, on to the lawn,
where, in the hush of a golden August evening
a reputation, 20 years tall, is put to the test.
So he takes extra care as yesterheroes must,
fires, and a dragonfly, incapsulated, bites the dust.
Then amidst bravos and tinkled applause,
blushing, Georgie leads them back indoors.

ROGER MCGOUGH

Poet's Corner

'George and the Dragonfly' is based part on truth, part on fantasy. There was a boy I knew at school who was gifted like the one in the poem (although his targets were not confined to dragonflies, and I doubt if he grew to acquire a taste for sherry and suntanned friends). Everybody is good at something, and I suppose this poem is about children being good at things which society later deems unimportant. And I think it's a pity.

Roger McGough

George and the Dragonfly — Your analysis

(1) Georgie Jennings made a great impression on the poet when he was a boy. Why was this so?

(2) Why did Georgie Jennings seem to be a rather unlikely hero?

(3) Did Georgie tend to skite about his skills? Write down a line or two to support your answer.

(4) Why is it possible to feel sad for Georgie?

(5) What is the meaning of, 'And talents such as spitting
           are considered unbefitting
           for upandcoming porkbutchers.'?

(6) In what ways did you find this poem different from others you have studied? Did you enjoy it more than other poems? Why?

(7) Explain the meaning of:
   (a) 'sherrytongued talk';
   (b) 'that shy sharpshooter of days gone by';
   (c) 'a dragonfly, incapsulated, bites the dust'.

Discussion Points

• Not all of us can be talented. But generally there is something that we can do rather well. Describe something that *you* do well, and enjoy doing.

• Do you know of someone who has an unusual skill or hobby? Describe it to the class in a few sentences.

THE YARN OF THE NANCY BELL

'Twas on the shores that round our coast
  From Deal to Ramsgate span,
That I found alone on a piece of stone
  An elderly naval man.

His hair was weedy, his beard was long,
  And weedy and long was he.
And I heard this wight on the shore recite,
  In a singular minor key:

'Oh, I am a cook and the captain bold,
  And the mate of the *Nancy* brig,
And a bo'sun tight, and a midshipmite,
  And the crew of the captain's gig.'

And he shook his fist and he tore his hair,
  Till I really felt afraid,
For I couldn't help thinking the man had been drinking,
  And so I simply said:

'Oh, elderly man, it's little I know
  Of the duties of men of the sea,
And I'll eat my hand if I understand
  How you can possibly be

'At once a cook, and a captain bold,
  And the mate of the *Nancy* brig,
And a bo'sun tight, and a midshipmite,
  And the crew of the captain's gig.'

Then he gave a hitch to his trousers, which
  Is a trick all seamen larn,
And having got rid of a thumping quid,
  He spun this painful yarn:

' 'Twas in the good ship *Nancy Bell*
  That we sailed to the Indian sea,
And there on a reef we come to grief,
  Which has often occurred to me.

'And pretty nigh all the crew was drowned
  (There was seventy-seven o' soul),
And only ten of the *Nancy's* men
  Said "Here!" to the muster-roll.

'There was me and the cook and the captain bold,
  And the mate of the *Nancy's* brig,
And the bo'sun tight, and a midshipmite,
  And the crew of the captain's gig.

'For a month we'd neither wittles nor drink,
  'Till a-hungry we did feel,
So we drawed a lot, and accordin' shot
  The captain for our meal.

'The next lot fell to the *Nancy's* mate,
  And a delicate dish he made;
Then our appetite with the midshipmite
  We seven survivors stayed.

'And then we murdered the bo'sun tight,
  And he much resembled pig;
Then we wittled free, did the cook and me,
  On the crew of the captain's gig.

'Then only the cook and me was left,
  And the delicate question, "Which
Of us goes to the kettle?" arose,
  And we argued it out as sich.

'For I loved that cook as a brother, I did,
  And the cook he worshipped me;
But we'd both be blowed if we'd either be stowed
  In the other chap's hold, you see.

' "I'll be eat if you dines off me," says Tom.
  "Yes, that", says I, "you'll be—
I'm boiled if I die, my friend," quoth I.
  And "Exactly so," quoth he.

'Says he, "Dear James, to murder me
  Were a foolish thing to do,
For don't you see that you can't cook *me*.
  While I can — and will — cook *you*!"

'So he boils the water, and takes the salt
    And the pepper in portions true
(Which he never forgot) and some chopped shallot,
    And some sage and parsley too.

' "Come here," says he, with a proper pride,
    Which his smiling features tell,
" 'Twill soothing be if I let you see
    How extremely nice you'll smell."

'And he stirred it round and round and round,
    And he sniffed at the foaming froth;
When I ups with his heels, and smothers his squeals
    In the scum of the boiling broth.

'And I eat that cook in a week or less,
    And — as I eating be
The last of his chops, why, I almost drops,
    For a vessel in sight I see.

'And I never larf, and I never smile,
    And I never lark nor play,
But sit and croak, and a single joke
    I have — which is to say:

'Oh, I am a cook and a captain bold,
    And the mate of the *Nancy* brig,
And a bo'sun tight, and a midshipmite,
    And the crew of the captain's gig!'

W. S. GILBERT

The Yarn of the Nancy Bell — Some essential vocabulary

Some of the words in the poem, especially the naval ones, are a little unfamiliar. If you read the poem closely, however, you'll be able to match most of them (left list) with their meanings (right list) below.

Words	Meanings
wight	midshipman — an apprentice officer
midshipmite	lump or wad of chewing tobacco
gig	person, creature
quid	tale or story
wittles	ship
yarn	boatswain or petty officer
bo'sun	small boat provided with oars and sails
brig	food (victuals)

Reading for details

(1) Quote the two lines that tell us how many of the men of the *Nancy Bell* were left after the ship struck the reef.

(2) Who were these survivors?

(3) How many men were there in the captain's gig?

(4) What decision did the survivors make when they were absolutely starving?

(5) What happened to the captain of the *Nancy Bell*?

(6) Finally there were only two men left. Who were they?

(7) What argument did the cook give to support his claim that he should be the last man alive?

(8) How did the sailor telling the story make sure that he, and not the cook, was the sole survivor?

(9) What do you think is amusing about this poem? Is it the story, or is it something about the way it is told?

from COLONEL FAZACKERLEY

Colonel Fazackerley Butterworth-Toast
Bought an old castle complete with a ghost,
But someone or other forgot to declare
To Colonel Fazack that the spectre was there.

On the very first evening, while waiting to dine,
The Colonel was taking a fine sherry wine,
When the ghost, with a furious flash and a flare,
Shot out of the chimney and shivered, 'Beware!'

Colonel Fazackerley put down his glass
And said, 'My dear fellow, that's really first class!
I just can't conceive how you do it at all.
I imagine you're going to a Fancy Dress Ball?'

At this, the dread ghost gave a withering cry.
Said the Colonel (his monocle firm in his eye),
'Now just how you do it I wish I could think.
Do sit down and tell me, and please have a drink.'

The ghost in his phosphorus cloak gave a roar
And floated about between ceiling and floor.
He walked through a wall and returned through a pane
And backed up the chimney and came down again.

Said the Colonel, 'With laughter I'm feeling quite weak!'
(As trickles of merriment ran down his cheek).
My house-warming party I hope you won't spurn.
You *must* say you'll come and you'll give us a turn!'

At this, the poor spectre — quite out of his wits —
Proceeded to shake himself almost to bits.
He rattled his chains and he clattered his bones
And he filled the whole castle with mumbles and moans.

But Colonel Fazackerley, just as before,
Was simply delighted and called out, 'Encore!'
At which the ghost vanished, his efforts in vain,
And never was seen at the castle again.

'Oh dear, what a pity!' said Colonel Fazack.
'I don't know his name, so I won't call him back.'
And then with a smile that was hard to define,
Colonel Fazackerley went in to dine.

CHARLES CAUSLEY

Colonel Fazackerley — Think about the ending
Why was the Colonel's smile 'hard to define'? Was he satisfied at the end, or not? Explain your answer.

Acting it out
A good way to enhance the humour of this poem is to have it acted out in your classroom. Have someone playing the part of, and saying the words spoken by, the Colonel; and have someone else imaginatively acting out the ghost's role. Weave the action and the Colonel's words together by using the whole class (or a section of the class) as the 'Narrator' reciting the poem.

Let your imagination go, and see what you come up with!

SIR SMASHAM UPPE

Good afternoon, Sir Smasham Uppe!
We're having tea: do take a cup!
Sugar and milk? Now let me see —
Two lumps, I think? . . . Good gracious me!
The silly thing slipped off your knee!
Pray don't apologise, old chap:
A very trivial mishap!
So clumsy of you? How absurd!
My dear Sir Smasham, not a word!
Now do sit down and have another,
And tell us all about your brother —
You know, the one who broke his head.
Is the poor fellow still in bed?
A chair — allow me sir! . . . Great Scott!
That *was* a nasty smash! Eh, what?
Oh, not at all: the chair was old —
Queen Anne, or so we have been told.
We've got at least a dozen more:
Just leave the pieces on the floor.
I want you to admire our view:
Come nearer to the window, do;
And look how beautiful . . . Tut, tut!
You didn't see that it was shut?
I hope you are not badly cut!
Not hurt? A fortunate escape!

Amazing! Not a single scrape!
And now, if you have finished tea,
I fancy you might like to see
A little thing or two I've got.
That china plate? Yes, worth a lot:
A beauty too . . . Ah, there it goes!
I trust it didn't hurt your toes?
Your elbow brushed it off the shelf?
Of course: I've done the same myself.
And now, my dear Sir Smasham — oh,
You surely don't intend to go?
You *must* be off? Well, come again.
So glad you're fond of porcelain!

E. V. RIEU

Sir Smasham Uppe — Two questions

(1) How does the host *appear* to feel about Sir Smasham?

(2) How does Sir Smasham feel about all his accidents?

Sir Smasham isn't the only one with this particular problem!

12. Alliteration

Alliteration is the commencing of two or more words close together with the same letter (or sound). Sometimes the repeated sound does the job of getting our attention; sometimes it adds a harsh note, a soft note, an enchanted note. Often, alliteration goes hand in hand with meaning. (Note: alliteration involves *consonant* and not *vowel* sounds).

Examples of alliteration

- *A*round the *r*ugged *r*ocks, the *r*agged *r*ascal *r*an.
- Out of the *d*ying *d*arkness, over the forest *d*im,
  The pearly *d*ew of the *d*awning clung to each giant limb.
- *F*ull *f*athom *f*ive thy *f*ather lies.
- Over the *c*obbles he *cl*attered and *cl*ashed in the dark inn-yard.
  (*Notice the onomatopoeia as well as the alliteration in this line.*)
- I am cold and alone,
  On my tree root *s*itting as *st*ill as *st*one.
- *Sh*eila i*s s*elling her *sh*op at the *s*ea*sh*ore
  But *sh*ops at the *s*ea*sh*ore are *s*ure hard to *s*ell.

Alliteration in the Comic Strips

Both of the following comic strips contain examples of alliteration. Write down the appropriate words and underline the letters being alliterated.

Tongue-Twisting

Here's a real tongue-twister of a poem for you. Try saying it to yourself. Do you know why it is so hard to say? Yes, it's the alliteration of the letter 'b'.

BETTY BOTTER

Betty Botter bought some butter,
But, she said, the butter's bitter;
If I put it in my batter
It will make my batter bitter,
But a bit of better butter's
Bound to make my batter better.
So she bought a bit of butter
Better than her bitter butter,
And she put it in her batter
And the batter wasn't bitter.
So 'twas better Betty Botter
Bought a bit of better butter.

ANONYMOUS

Alliteration in Poetry and Speech

Poets often use alliteration to create all kinds of effects, feelings, moods and movements. But many of our everyday phrases and expressions also employ alliteration. Let's examine both of these aspects.

Find the alliteration

Look at this list of 20 quotations collected from a wide range of popular poems. Write them down and underline the examples of alliteration.

(1) I have seen old ships sail like swans asleep.

(2) Not a drum was heard, not a funeral note.

(3) He clasps the crag with crooked hands;
     Close to the sun in lonely lands.

(4) The Assyrian came down like the wolf on the fold.

(5) I sprang to the stirrup, and Joris, and he.

(6) Only the stuttering rifles' rapid rattle.

(7) But crackle-dry as wing of dragonfly.

(8) Take the big roller's shoulder, speed and swerve,
     Come to the long beach home like a gull diving.

(9) Its quick soft silver bell beating, beating.

(10) My love is like a red, red rose.

(11) Glory be to God for dappled things.

(12) Blow, bugle, blow, set the wild echoes flying.

(13) A score of troopers were scattering wide
     And a hundred more were ready to ride.

(14) 'Who touches a hair of yon head
     Dies like a dog! March on!' he said.

(15) Water, water, everywhere,
     Nor any drop to drink.

(16) The Lotus blooms below the barren peak.

(17) The league-long roller thundering on the reef.

(18) When men were all asleep the snow came flying.

(19) Eyes full of sparkling wickedness, ears finely cut, flexibly moving.

(20) The Miller was a chap of sixteen stone,
     A great stout fellow big in brawn and bone.

Complete the common couples

There are quite a few well-known alliteration couples — e.g. *l*ife and *l*imb, *h*ouse and *h*ome, and so on. See whether you can supply the missing partner for each of the following.

spick and ....

.... and sound

thick and ....

.... and proper

rough and ....

.... and don'ts

fast and ....

.... and turn

hale and ....

.... and that

sweet and ....

.... and roll

rant and ....

.... and tested

wild and ....

.... and hers

wash and ....

.... and cheese

black and ....

.... and steady

home and ....

.... and bred

sticks and ....

.... and dash

tried and ....

.... and stripes

pots and ....

.... and slide

birds and ....

.... and spice

trials and ....

.... and baggage

13. Poems to Compare

'The Last of His Tribe' and 'Then and Now' are both concerned with the passing of time. In the first of the two poems, the Aboriginal warrior thinks back to the happy life he had with his wife and tribe, who have perished. In the second, Aboriginal poet Kath Walker is pointing out that the Aborigines were far happier in the past, before they became exposed to the white man's way of life.

THE LAST OF HIS TRIBE

He crouches and buries his face on his knees,
    And hides in the dark of his hair;
For he cannot look up to the storm-smitten trees,
    Or think of the loneliness there —
    Of the loss and the loneliness there.

The wallaroos grope through the tufts of the grass,
    And turn to their coverts for fear;
But he sits in the ashes and lets them pass
    Where the boomerangs sleep with the spear —
    With the nullah, the sling, and the spear.

Uloola, behold him! The thunder that breaks
    On the tops of the rocks with the rain,
And the wind which drives up with the salt of the lakes,
    Have made him a hunter again —
    A hunter and fisher again.

For his eyes have been full with a smouldering thought;
    But he dreams of the hunts of yore,
And of foes that he sought, and of fights that he fought
    With those who will battle no more —
    Who will go to the battle no more.

It is well that the water which tumbles and fills
    Goes moaning and moaning along;
For an echo rolls out from the sides of the hills,
    And he starts at a wonderful song —
    At the sound of a wonderful song.

And he sees through the rents of the scattering fogs
    The corroboree warlike and grim,
And the lubra who sat by the fire on the logs,
    To watch, like a mourner, for him —
    Like a mother and mourner for him.

Will he go in his sleep from these desolate lands,
    Like a chief, to the rest of his race,
With the honey-voiced woman who beckons and stands,
    And gleams like a dream in his face —
    Like a marvellous dream in his face?

HENRY KENDALL

The Last of His Tribe — Feelings

Draw up the table and see whether you can find phrases and sentences from
the poem to match up with the feelings listed.

Feelings	Phrases and Sentences
Despair	
Fear	
Happiness	
Sadness	
Loneliness	

from THEN AND NOW

In my dreams I hear my tribe
Laughing as they hunt and swim,
But dreams are shattered by rushing car,
By grinding tram and hissing train,
And I see no more my tribe of old
As I walk alone in the teeming town.

I have seen corroboree
Where that factory belches smoke;
Here where they have memorial park
One time lubras dug for yams;
One time our dark children played
There where the railway yards are now,
And where I remember the didgeridoo
Calling us to dance and play,
Offices now, neon lights now,
Bank and shop and advertisement now,
Traffic and trade of the busy town.

No more woomera, no more boomerang,
No more play about, no more the old ways,
Children of nature we were then,
No clocks hurrying crowds to toil.
Now I am civilised and work in the white way,
Now I have dress, now I have shoes;
Isn't she lucky to have a good job!
Better when I had only a dillybag.
Better when I had nothing but happiness.

KATH WALKER

Then and Now — Facts

By referring to 'Then and Now', complete the table. The first one has been done to help you.

Then	Now
corroboree	factory belches smoke
lubras dug for yams	
dark children played here	
the didgeridoo calling us to dance and play	
better when I had only a dillybag	

The subject of mosquitoes is a popular one with poets. Can you suggest why? While you're thinking about it, here are two mosquito poems for you to compare.

MOSQUITOES

Mosquitoes are blood relations
They doze on the white ceiling
Like the children upstairs
While we wake below

We are their livelihood
They wish us no harm
Stealing through windows
With their fine instruments
And teething drone
There they say you hardly felt it

And they work like surgeons
While we stir in sleep
Tapping veins adjusting
The flow dim
Figures at work murmuring
Creatures of the subconscious

Extinct cloaked vampires
Spirits hooked on blood
Live scarlet drops
Hanging like fruit bats
From the ceiling — our babies
Our own flesh and blood
Loving us and jealous
Mmmmmm they cry at dusk
They are helpless without us.

DAVID CAMPBELL

Mosquitoes — One view
(1) Why does David Campbell refer to mosquitoes as 'blood relations'?
(2) How are the mosquitoes 'like surgeons'?
(3) 'Live scarlet drops' — When are mosquitoes like this?
(4) 'From the ceiling — our babies' seems an incredible statement. Can you suggest why the poet calls the mosquitoes 'our babies'?

(5) What do vampires do? Do you think the poet is justified in referring to the mosquitoes as vampires?
(6) Why are mosquitoes 'helpless without us'?

MOSQUITO

On the fine wire of his whine he walked,
Unseen in the ominous bedroom dark.
A traitor to his camouflage, he talked
A thirsty blue streak distinct as a spark.

I was to him a fragrant lake of blood
From which he had to sip a drop or die.
A reservoir, a lavish field of food,
I lay awake, unconscious of size.

We seemed fair-matched opponents. Soft he dropped
Down like an anchor on his thread of song.
His nose sank thankfully in; then I slapped
At the sting on my arm, cunning and strong.

A cunning, strong Gargantua, I struck
When he was pinned in the feast of my flesh,
Lulled by my blood, relaxed, half-sated, stuck,
Engrossed in the gross rivers of myself.

Success! Without a cry the creature died,
Became a fleck of fluff upon the sheet.
The small welt of remorse subsides as side
By side we, murderer and murdered, sleep.

JOHN UPDIKE

Mosquito — Another view

(1) Explain why the mosquito was a 'traitor to his camouflage'.
(2) Find a line in the first stanza that reminds you of the *sound* a mosquito makes.
(3) Explain what the poet means by the simile, 'Down like an anchor on his thread of song.'
(4) In what way is the person in this poem 'cunning'?
(5) Who are the 'murderer' and 'murdered' in the last line? How does their 'sleep' differ?
(6) Which poem about mosquitoes did you prefer — David Campbell's or John Updike's? Can you explain why?

It has been suggested that Robert Browning wrote this poem while on board a ship travelling to Italy. The up-and-down motion of the waves supposedly brought to Browning's mind the movement of a horse galloping along.

The town of Ghent is in Belgium and Aix-la-Chapelle is just over the border in France. But there is no historical evidence for the events of the poem. Moreover, the distance between the two towns is more than fifty miles, which seems rather far for any horse to gallop at the pace that would have been required.

The poem owes much of its success to its rhythmic beat. When you read it aloud you can almost feel yourself riding along at great speed on one of the horses.

HOW THEY BROUGHT THE GOOD NEWS FROM GHENT TO AIX
[16—]

I sprang to the stirrup, and Joris, and he;
I galloped, Dirck galloped, we galloped all three;
'Good speed!' cried the watch, as the gate-bolts undrew;
'Speed!' echoed the wall to us galloping through;
Behind shut the postern,[1] the lights sank to rest,
And into the midnight we galloped abreast.

Not a word to each other; we kept the great pace
Neck by neck, stride by stride, never changing our place;
I turned in my saddle and made its girths tight,
Then shortened each stirrup, and set the pique[2] right,
Rebuckled the cheek-strap, chained slacker the bit,
Nor galloped less steadily Roland a whit.

1   *postern:* a small (back) gate.
2   *pique:* usually 'peak' — the highest part of the saddle-bow.

'Twas moonset at starting; but while we drew near
Lokeren, the cocks crew and twilight dawned clear;
At Boom, a great yellow star came out to see;
At Düffeld, 'twas morning as plain as could be;
And from the Mecheln church-steeple we heard the half-chime,
So Joris broke silence with, 'Yet there is time!'

At Aerschot, up leaped of a sudden the sun,
And against him the cattle stood black every one,
To stare thro' the mist at us galloping past,
And I saw my stout galloper Roland at last,
With resolute shoulders, each butting away
The haze, as some bluff river headland its spray.

And his low head and crest, just one sharp ear bent back
For my voice, and the other pricked out on his track;
And one eye's black intelligence, — ever that glance
O'er its white edge at me, his own master, askance![3]
And the thick heavy spume-flakes which aye and anon[4]
His fierce lips shook upwards in galloping on.

By Hasselt, Dirck groaned; and cried Joris, 'Stay spur!
Your Roos galloped bravely, the fault's not in her,
We'll remember at Aix' — for one heard the quick wheeze
Of her chest, saw the stretched neck and staggering knees,
And sunk tail, and horrible heave of the flank,
As down on her haunches she shuddered and sank.

So we were left galloping, Joris and I,
Past Looz and past Tongres, no cloud in the sky;
The broad sun above laughed a pitiless laugh,
'Neath our feet broke the brittle bright stubble like chaff;
Till over by Dalhem a dome-spire sprang white,
And 'Gallop,' gasped Joris, 'for Aix is in sight!'

'How they'll greet us!' — and all in a moment his roan
Rolled neck and croup[5] over, lay dead as a stone;
And there was my Roland to bear the whole weight
Of the news which alone could save Aix from her fate,
With his nostrils like pits full of blood to the brim,
And with circles of red for his eye-sockets' rim.

3 *askance:* sideways, i.e. out of the corner of his eye.
4 *aye and anon:* frequently, constantly.
5 *croup:* the rump of a horse. To 'roll over neck and croup' means to
   tumble over completely.

Then I cast loose my buffcoat, each holster let fall,
Shook off both my jack-boots, let go belt and all,
Stood up in the stirrup, leaned, patted his ear,
Called my Roland his pet-name, my horse without peer;
Clapped my hands, laughed and sang, any noise, bad or good,
Till at length into Aix Roland galloped and stood.

And all I remember is, friends flocking round
As I sat with his head 'twixt my knees on the ground;
And no voice but was praising this Roland of mine,
As I poured down his throat our last measure of wine,
Which (the burgesses voted by common consent)
Was no more than his due who brought good news from Ghent.

ROBERT BROWNING

The next poem is a parody of 'How They Brought the Good News from
Ghent to Aix'. What is a parody? A parody imitates the characteristics of
an original (poem, song, voice, etc) in order to make it appear ridiculous,
while making the parody itself appear clever, funny and perhaps effective
in conveying a message of some sort. Notice that the Yeatman and Sellar
poem has rhythm and rhyme patterns similar to those of the Browning poem.
However, the original was serious and dramatic, describing the saving of Aix
from a great catastrophe; whereas the parody is full of ridiculous and farcical
happenings.

from HOW I BROUGHT THE GOOD NEWS FROM AIX
TO GHENT (OR VICE VERSA)

I sprang to the rollocks and Jorrocks and me,
And I galloped, you galloped, he galloped, we galloped all three . . .
Not a word to each other; we kept changing place,
Neck to neck, back to front, ear to ear, face to face;
And we yelled once or twice, when we heard a clock chime,
'Would you kindly oblige us, *Is that the right time?*'
As I galloped, you galloped, he galloped, we galloped, ye galloped, they
    two shall have galloped; *let us trot.*

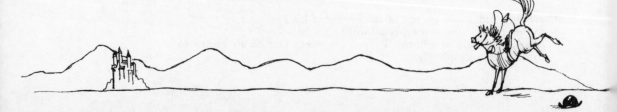

I unsaddled the saddle, unbuckled the bit,
Unshackled the bridle (the thing didn't fit)
And ungalloped, ungalloped, ungalloped, ungalloped a bit.
Then I cast off my bluff-coat, let my bowler hat fall,
Took off both my boots and my trousers and all —
Drank off my stirrup-cup, felt a bit tight,
And unbridled the saddle: it still wasn't right.

Then all I remember is, things reeling round
As I sat with my head 'twixt my ears on the ground —
For imagine my shame when they asked what I meant
And I had to confess that I'd been, gone and went
And *forgotten the news* I was bringing to Ghent,
Though I'd galloped and galloped and galloped and galloped and
    galloped
And galloped and galloped and galloped. (Had I not would have been
    galloped?)

Envoi

So I sprang to a taxi and shouted 'To Aix!'
And he blew on his horn and he threw off his brakes,
And all the way back till my money was spent
We rattled and rattled and rattled and rattled and rattled
And rattled and rattled —
And eventually sent a telegram.

R. J. YEATMAN and W. C. SELLAR

Bringing the Good News — Pick the parody

Copy down the following lines from Browning's poem, then match them up with the corresponding humorous lines from the Yeatman and Sellar poem.

Browning	Yeatman and Sellar
(1) We kept the great pace	
(2) 'Yet there is time!'	
(3) chained slacker the bit	
(4) Then I cast loose my buffcoat, each holster let fall	
(5) Shook off both my jack-boots, let go belt and all	
(6) As I sat with his head 'twixt my knees on the ground	

Here are two poems about snakes. The two poets take a very different approach to their subject. Their reasons for having written the poems make interesting reading.

SNAKE

Suddenly the grass before my feet
shakes and becomes alive.
The snake
twists, almost leaps,
graceful even in terror,
smoothness looping back over smoothness,
slithers away, disappears.
And the grass is again still.

And surely, by whatever means of communication
is available to snakes,
the word is passed:
Hey, I just met a man, a monster, too;
Must have been, oh, seven feet tall
So keep away from the long grass,
it's dangerous there.

IAN MUDIE

Poet's Corner

I met the snake at Sellicks Beach (South Australia). It was only a small one. When the man I was with started telling everyone to keep away from the long grass as there was a big snake there I began to wonder what the snake was thinking. That night I wrote the poem.

Ian Mudie

THE KILLER

The day was clear as fire,
the birds sang frail as glass,
when thirsty I came to the creek
and fell by its side in the grass.

My breast on the bright moss
and shower-embroidered weeds,
my lips to the live water
I saw him turn in the reeds.

Black horror sprang from the dark
in a violent birth,
and through its cloth of grass
I felt the clutch of earth.

O beat him into the ground.
O strike him till he dies —
or else your life itself
drains through those colourless eyes.

I struck again and again.
Slender in black and red
he lies, and his icy glance
turns outward, clear and dead.

But nimble my enemy
as water is, or wind.
He has slipped from his death aside
and vanished into my mind.

He has vanished whence he came,
my nimble enemy;
and the ants come out to the snake
and drink at his shallow eye.

JUDITH WRIGHT

Poet's Corner

I had not realised that my fear came from inside me and was not solved
by killing the snake, but would stay inside me and might lead to my
killing other innocent creatures — that, in fact, my fear was my enemy,
and not the snake at all. ... The poem was a way of making myself
realise that fear is what must be conquered, not anything in the outside
world that makes us afraid.

Judith Wright

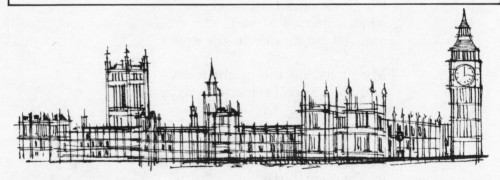

William Wordsworth, on 31 July 1802, was so excited, delighted and
enthralled by the sight of the city that he wrote a poem that very day to
show the depth of his feelings.

On the other hand, a modern poet — Murray Jennings — was so disgusted
with the view of Sydney from Pyrmont Bridge that he wrote a poem con-
demning what he saw. In doing this, he was obviously very mindful of
Wordsworth's original.

UPON WESTMINSTER BRIDGE

Earth has not anything to show more fair:
Dull would he be of soul who could pass by
A sight so touching in its majesty:
This City now doth, like a garment, wear
The beauty of the morning; silent, bare,
Ships, towers, domes, theatres, and temples lie
Open unto the fields, and to the sky;
All bright and glittering in the smokeless air.
Never did sun more beautifully steep
In his first splendour, valley, rock, or hill;
Ne'er saw I, never felt, a calm so deep!
The river glideth at his own sweet will:
Dear God! the very houses seem asleep;
And all that mighty heart is lying still!

WILLIAM WORDSWORTH

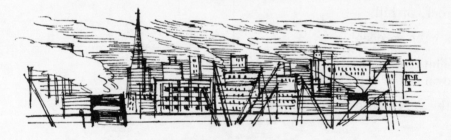

UPON PYRMONT BRIDGE

Earth has not anything to show less fair:
Dulled are we-of-the-soul who do pass by
A sight so touching in its tragedy:
This City now does like a garment wear
The hot breath of the morning traffic there;
Ships, towers, domes, theatres, and plazas lie
Open unto the fumes that hang in the sky;
All blanched and jaundiced in the smog-filled air.
Never did sun more encumbered steep
In his first grey-brown halo, old, and chill;
Ne'er saw I, never felt, a panic so deep!
The harbour chokes now in its own sour fill;
Dear God! the very buildings stand as cheap
Reminders of that mighty heart soon lying still!

MURRAY JENNINGS

Upon Two Bridges — Positives and negatives

In the left-hand column, words and phrases from 'Upon Westminster Bridge' have been set out. All of them have *positive* associations. See whether you can insert, next to them, the corresponding words and phrases from 'Upon Pyrmont Bridge', with their *negative* associations. The first one has been done to help you.

'Upon Westminster Bridge'	'Upon Pyrmont Bridge'
more fair	less fair
majesty	
The beauty of the morning	
Open unto the fields, and to the sky	
All bright and glittering in the smokeless air	
In his first splendour, valley, rock, or hill	
a calm so deep!	
The river glideth at his own sweet will	
the very houses seem asleep	

Did you get the impression that certain things have changed since 1802?

14. Personification

In literature, and particularly in poetry, some *things* are often considered as if they were alive, although they in fact are not. Look carefully at these examples.

- The headlights winked in the gathering dusk.
- Gentle breezes stroked our faces.
- Fire walked across the hill.

The headlights, breezes and fire have taken on *human* qualities. This is **personification**, the giving of living qualities such as habits, actions, feelings, thoughts — even *personalities* — to things that are not human.

Read through the poem 'The Frowning Cliff'.

THE FROWNING CLIFF

The sea has a laugh
And the cliff a frown;
For the laugh of the sea
Is wearing him down.

Lipping and lapping
Frown as he may,
The laughing sea
Will eat him away;

Knees and body,
And tawny head,
He'll smile at last
On a golden bed.

HERBERT ASQUITH

The Frowning Cliff — Think, write and draw

(1) What human qualities is the sea given in this poem?
(2) What human characteristics is the cliff given?

(3)   Why does the sea have a laugh?
(4)   Why is the poem called 'The Frowning Cliff?'
(5)   Try to explain what the last stanza is suggesting will happen.
(6)   Draw a picture in which you give human qualities to the sea and the cliff.

Here is another poem. This time a watch is being personified.

THE WATCH

When I
took my
watch to the watchfixer I
felt privileged but also pained to watch the operation. He
had long fingernails and a voluntary squint. He
fixed a magnifying cup over his
squint eye. He
undressed my
watch. I
watched him
split her
in three layers and lay her
middle — a quivering viscera — in a circle on a little plinth. He
shoved shirt sleeves up and leaned like an ogre over my
naked watch. With critical pincers he
poked and stirred. He
lifted out little private things with a magnet too tiny for me
to watch almost. 'Watch out!' I
almost said. His
eye watched, enlarged, the secrets of my
watch, and I
watched anxiously. Because what if he
touched her
ticker too rough, and she
gave up the ghost out of pure fright? Or put her
things back backwards so she'd
run backwards after this? Or he
might lose a minuscule part, connected to her
exquisite heart, and mix her
up, instead of fix her.

And all the time,
all the time-
pieces on the walls, on the shelves, told the time,
told the time
in swishes and ticks,
swishes and ticks,
and seemed to be gloating, as they watched and told. I
felt faint, I
was about to lose my breath — my
ticker going lickety-split — when watchfixer clipped her
three slices together with a gleam and two flicks of his
tools like chopsticks. He
spat out his
eye, lifted her
high, gave her
a twist, set her
hands right, and laid her
little face, quite as usual, in its place on my
wrist.

MAY SWENSON

The Watch — Four questions and a sketch
(1) What words tell you that the watch is female?
(2) The word 'operation' suggests that the watch is human. What word or words would normally be used in place of 'operation'?
(3) The watchmaker opens up the watch, and the poet continues with the personification. Find as many human terms as you can that are applied to the inner mechanism of the watch.
(4) Even the other timepieces on the wall are personified. What words show you this?
(5) Draw a picture of the watch in its personified state.

More examples of personification

Here are some further examples of personification. Explain how each of the words in heavy type is personified (given human qualities).

(1)   The **sun** peeped over the window-sill.
(2)   **Stars** winked in the heavens.
(3)   The **trees** sighed.
(4)   The **river** moaned.
(5)   The **fog** crept up from the sea.
(6)   The **wind** howled around the house.
(7)   The **brook** chattered over the stones.
(8)   **Leaves** danced in the breeze.
(9)   The **tree-tops** kissed.
(10)   Softly sing the **waters**.
(11)   The **flames** of the bushfire raced across the hill.
(12)   The old **door-hinge** groaned.

15. Feelings

STUFF

Lovers lie around in it
Broken glass is found in it
Grass
I like that stuff

Tuna fish get trapped in it
Legs come wrapped in it
Nylon
I like that stuff

Eskimos and tramps chew it
Madame Tussaud gave status to it
Wax
I like that stuff

Elephants get sprayed with it
Scotch is made with it
Water
I like that stuff

Clergy are dumbfounded by it
Bones are surrounded by it
Flesh
I like that stuff

Harps are strung with it
Mattresses are sprung with it
Wire
I like that stuff

Carpenters make cots of it
Undertakers use lots of it
Wood
I like that stuff

Cigarettes are lit by it
Pensioners get happy when they sit by it
Fire
I like that stuff

Dankworth's alto is made of it, most of it
Scoobdedoo is composed of it
Plastic
I like that stuff

Man made fibres and raw materials
Old rolled gold and breakfast cereals
Platinum linoleum
I like that stuff

Skin on my hands
Hair on my head
Toenails on my feet
And linen on my bed

Well I like that stuff
Yes I like that stuff
The earth
Is made of earth
And I like that stuff.

ADRIAN MITCHELL

Stuff — About the poem

This is a simple poem — a poem of celebration. The poet is celebrating the 'stuff' of life — the materials out of which are made things that he enjoys. Because he enjoys the end-product (for example, the cool jazz of John Dankworth's alto saxophone) he celebrates the 'stuff' out of which it is made — plastic.

Try your hand

What are some of the things *you* like in life? What materials are they made of? Write a celebratory poem in which you honour the 'stuff' of which these things you enjoy are made.

CLOTHES

My mother keeps telling me
When she was in her teens
She wore quite different clothes from mine
And hadn't heard of jeans,

T-shirts, no hats, and dresses that
Reach far above our knees.
I laughed at first and then I thought
One day my kids will tease

And scoff at what *I'm* wearing now.
What will *their* fashions be?
I'd give an awful lot to know,
To look ahead and see.

Girls dressed like girls perhaps once more
And boys no longer half
Resembling us. Oh, what's in store
To make *our* children laugh?

ELIZABETH JENNINGS

Clothes — Getting behind the poem

(1) Why do you think the girl's mother *keeps* telling her how girls' clothing used to be quite different?

(2) How do you think the mother feels about her daughter's clothes?

(3) What is it that causes the girl to stop laughing at her mother's words?

(4) What is it that the poet would 'give an awful lot to know'?

(5) 'Girls dressed like girls perhaps once more', writes the poet. She seems to have some fixed ideas about what girls should wear. How do you think she imagines that a girl dressed like a girl would look?

(6) What things is she speaking of when she refers to boys 'half resembling' girls?

(7) Why does she expect that children in future years will laugh at *her* fashions?

(8) In one or two sentences explain the *theme* of this poem — the message the poet wants to convey.

Sometimes it's hard to imagine people involved in activities other than the ones in which we are accustomed to seeing them. It may be hard to imagine a bank manager riding a trail-bike, or an insurance salesman out hang-gliding. This poem describes the reaction of a person upon hearing that his teacher has a go at fishing.

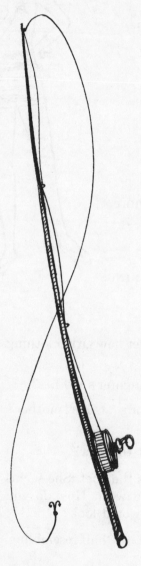

HE DON'T KNOW THE *INSIDE* FEEL

My teacher fish!
You must be screwed up, man.
A teacher? Hell
A teacher TEACHES.
He don't know the outdoor stuff.
He don't care.
He'd never walk by himself
Before breakfast
Across fields
Gettin his feet soaked
Just to fish!
He's a teacher.
He teaches.

He marks papers
Or he reads books.
He don't fish with no 2-ounce rod
And lay that long line easy on the top
Like this here ... Look!
Oh, man
Don't tell me he hears them wild birds.
He don't.
He don't know the *inside* feel
Of white water rushin
Cold against his knees.
He don't know fishin, man.
Not like me.

HERBERT R. ADAMS

Getting inside
(1) How does this person feel about his teacher?
(2) (i) Find *an action* that the poet thinks his teacher couldn't ever carry out.
     (ii) Find *a sound* that he feels his teacher wouldn't have heard.

(iii)   Find *a feeling* that he doesn't believe his teacher has experienced.

(3)   This person believes that fishing is something special. Why? What does it really mean to him.

Remember what it was like on *your* first day at a new school? Here's one person's description of the experience.

THE NEW BOY

The door swung inward. I stood and breathed
The new-school atmosphere.
The smell of polish and disinfectant,
And the flavour of my own fear.

I followed into the cloakroom; the walls
Rang to the shattering noise
Of boys who barged and boys who banged;
Boys and still more boys!

A boot flew by me. Its angry owner
Pursued with force and yell;
Somewhere a man snapped orders; somewhere
There clanged a warning bell.

And there I hung with my new schoolmates;
They pushing and shoving me; I
Unknown, unwanted, pinned to the wall;
On the verge of ready-to-cry.

Then, from the doorway, a boy called out:
'Hey, you over there! You're new!
Don't just stand there propping the wall up!
I'll look after you!'

I turned; I timidly raised my eyes;
He stood and grinned meanwhile;
And my fear died, and my lips answered
Smile for his smile.

He showed me the basins, the rows of pegs;
He hung my cap at the end;
He led me away to my new classroom ...
And now that boy's my friend.

JOHN WALSH

The New Boy — Understanding

(1)   What are three things the new boy notices when he first enters the school?

(2)   What causes the new boy to be 'pinned to the wall'?

(3)   What sort of boy does he appear to be?

(4)   From what he says, what sort of person does the boy who 'called out' seem to be?

(5)   What is the effect of the 'old' boy's smile on the new boy?

Appreciating

(6)   The first sentence is short. What effect is thus achieved?

(7)   What is the effect of the line, 'On the verge of ready-to-cry.'?

(8)   The poet has sought to re-create certain emotions with his poem. What are they? As far as you're concerned, has he succeeded?

Discussion Point

Organise a class discussion on 'The Problems of Fitting into a New School'. List the problems and discuss ways of overcoming them. If any suggestions seem particularly worthwhile you might be able to pass them on through your School Council.

ROUGH

My parents kept me from children who were rough
Who threw words like stones and who wore torn clothes.
Their thighs showed through rags. They ran in the street
And climbed cliffs and stripped by the country streams.

I feared more than tigers their muscles like iron
Their jerking hands and their knees tight on my arms.
I feared the salt coarse pointing of those boys
Who copied my lisp behind me on the road.

They were lithe, they sprang out behind hedges
Like dogs to bark at my world. They threw mud
While I looked the other way, pretending to smile.
I longed to forgive them, but they never smiled.

STEPHEN SPENDER

Rough — Analysing feelings

(1)   What did the poet's parents fear about contact between their son and the 'rough' children?

(2) How did the poet feel about the rough children? Upon what evidence do you base your view?

(3) How did the rough children feel about Stephen Spender? How did they show their feelings?

(4) What action of the rough ones made Spender feel locked out of their world?

(5) What feelings are aroused in you towards
   (i)   Spender?
   (ii) the rough children?
How does the poet arouse these feelings?

ONE SUMMER

One summer you
aeroplaned away,
too much money
away for me, and
stayed there for
quite a few
missed embraces.

Before leaving
you smiled me that
you'd return all of
a mystery moment and
would airletter me
every few breakfasts
in the meantime.
           This
you did, and I thank
you most kissingly.
              I
wish however, that I
could hijackerplane
to the Ignited States
of Neon where I'd
crash land perfectly
in the deserted
airport of your heart.

STEVE TURNER

One Summer — Unusual use of language

This poem contains many examples of unusual use of language. Instead of using *ordinary* words and phrases, the poet uses *fresh* words and phrases. Their interest-level is higher, and frequently they compress language and 'save' words.

Look at the following table and you will see an example of this. 'Aeroplaned away' is a fresh way of saying 'flew away in an aeroplane'. Draw up the table in your exercise book and work out an ordinary way of expressing each of the 'fresh' phrases or words from the poem.

Poet's 'fresh' phrase	An 'ordinary' way of saying it
(1) 'aeroplaned away'	flew away in an aeroplane
(2) 'too much money away'	
(3) 'for quite a few missed embraces'	
(4) 'you smiled me'	
(5) 'you'd return all of a mystery moment'	
(6) 'airletter me'	
(7) 'every few breakfasts in the meantime'	
(8) 'I thank you most kissingly'	
(9) 'hijackerplane'	
(10) 'Ignited States of Neon'	
(11) 'where I'd crash land perfectly'	

Ideally the humorous poetry of Pam Ayres should be read aloud, so get one of your good class-readers (someone who's a bit of an actor or actress) to read for the class.

OH NO, I GOT A COLD

I am sitting on the sofa,
By the fire and staying in,
Me head is free of comfort
And me nose is free of skin.
Me friends have run for cover,
They have left me pale and sick
With me pockets full of tissues
And me nostrils full of Vick.

That bloke in the telly adverts,
He's supposed to have a cold,
He has a swig of whatnot
And he drops off, good as gold,
His face like snowing harvest
Slips into sweet repose,
Well, I bet this tortured breathing
Never whistled down his nose.

I burnt me bit of dinner
Cause I've lost me sense of smell,
But then, I couldn't taste it,
So that worked out very well.
I'd buy some, down the café,
But I know that at the till,
A voice from work will softly say
'I thought that you were ill'.

So I'm wrapped up in a blanket
With me feet up on a stool,
I've watched the telly programmes
And the kids come home from school,
But what I haven't watched for
Is any sympathy,
Cause all you ever get is:
'Oh no, keep away from me!'

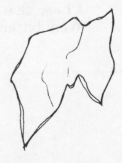

Medicinal discovery,
It moves in mighty leaps,
It leapt straight past the common cold
And gave it us for keeps.
Now I'm not a fussy woman,
There's no malice in me eye
But I wish that they could cure
the common cold. That's all. Goodbye.

PAM AYRES

Analysing the humour of Pam Ayres
Look at each of the following aspects of the poem and decide how much each of them contributes to the poem:
(1) the reader's voice;
(2) the subject of the poem;
(3) the language of the poem;
(4) the rhythm of the poem.

Try your hand
Write your own Pam Ayres–type poem, starting off with 'Oh no, me shoelace broke'.

ANCIENT HISTORY

I hope the old Romans
Had painful abdomens.

I hope that the Greeks
Had toothache for weeks.

I hope the Egyptians
Had chronic conniptions.

I hope that the Arabs
Were bitten by scarabs.

I hope that the Vandals
Had thorns in their sandals.

I hope that the Persians
Had gout in all versions.

I hope that the Medes
Were kicked by their steeds.

They started the fuss
And left it to us!

ARTHUR GUITERMAN

Ancient History — Two quick queries
(1)   'And left it to us!' What did 'they' leave to 'us'?
(2)   How does the poet feel about Ancient History?

For you to try
Pick out your most un-favourite school subject and identify those whose
fault it all is. Now try your own hand at writing a poem in the style of
'Ancient History', beginning 'I hope ...' Read your completed efforts to the
whole class.

A BOY AND HIS STOMACH

What's the matter with you — ain't I always been your friend?
Ain't I been a pardner to you? All my pennies don't I spend
In gettin' nice things for you? Don't I give you lots of cake?
Say, stummick, what's the matter, that you had to go and ache?

Why, I loaded you with good things; yesterday I gave you more
Potatoes, squash an' turkey than you'd ever had before.
I gave you nuts and candy, pumpkin pie an' chocolate cake,
An' las' night when I got to bed you had to go an' ache.

Say, what's the matter with you — ain't you satisfied at all?
I gave you all you wanted, you was hard jes' like a ball,
An' you couldn't hold another bit of puddin', yet las' night
You ached mo' awful, stummick; that ain't treatin' me jes' right.

I've been a friend to you, I have, why ain't you a friend o' mine?
They gave me castor oil last night because you made me whine.
I'm awful sick this mornin' an' I'm feelin' mighty blue,
Because you don't appreciate the things I do for you.

EDGAR GUEST

A Boy and His Stomach — Diagnosis

Using clues contained in the poem, answer the following questions and so complete your assessment of the poet's condition.

Question	Answer	Line which gives you a clue
(1) How old do you estimate this boy to be?		
(2) How well educated does this boy appear to be?		
(3) What seems to have caused his problems?		
(4) What treatment has he received already?		
(5) What does he seem to be complaining about?		

Treatment

In order to remedy the boy's condition and cure his stomach-ache, try writing your own poem on the subject. If you wish, draw upon your personal experiences.

16. Some Grave Poems

LESLIE MOORE

Here lies what's left
Of Leslie Moore.
    No Les
    No more.

A DENTIST

Stranger, approach this spot with gravity:
John Brown is filling his last cavity.

THE OPTIMIST

The optimist fell ten stories.
    At each window bar
He shouted to his friends:
    'All right so far.'

THE BIRD MAN

There was an old man who averred
He had learnt how to fly like a bird.
Cheered by thousands of people
He leapt from the steeple —
This tomb states the date it occurred.

PASSING

He passed the bobby without any fuss,
And he passed the cart of hay.
He tried to pass a swerving bus,
And then he passed away.

MIKE O'DAY

This is the grave of Mike O'Day
Who died maintaining his right of way.
His right was clear, his will was strong,
But he's just as dead as if he'd been wrong.

EZRA POUND

Here lies the body of Ezra P
Lost at sea and never found.

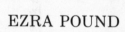

MARTIN ELGINBRODDE

Here lie I, Martin Elginbrodde:
Ha'e mercy on my soul, Lord God,
As I wad do, were I Lord God
And ye were Martin Elginbrodde.

ARABELLA YOUNG

Beneath this stone
A lump of clay
Lies Arabella Young
Who on the 21st of May
1771
Began to hold her tongue.

AN EPITAPH AT GREAT TORRINGTON, DEVON

Here lies a man who was killed by lightning;
He died when his prospects seemed to be brightening.
He might have cut a flash in this world of trouble,
But the flash cut him, and he lies in the stubble.

17. Birds of Feather

THE BATTERY HEN

Oh, I am a battery hen,
On me back there's not a germ,
I never scratched a farmyard,
And I never pecked a worm,
I never had the sunshine,
To warm me feathers through,
Eggs I lay. Every day.
For the likes of you.

When you has them scrambled,
Piled up on your plate,
It's me what you should thank for that,
I never lays them late,
I always lays them reg'lar,
I always lays them right,
I never lays them brown,
I always lays them white.

But it's no life, for a battery hen,
In me box I'm sat,
A funnel stuck out from the side,
Me pellets comes down that,
I gets a squirt of water,
Every half a day,
Watchin' with me beady eye,
Me eggs, roll away.

I lays them in a funnel,
Strategically placed,
So that I don't kick 'em,
And let them go to waste,
They rolls off down the tubing,
And up the gangway quick,
Sometimes I gets to thinkin'
'That could have been a chick!'

I might have been a farmyard hen,
Scratchin' in the sun,
There might have been a crowd of chicks,
After me to run,
There might have been a cockerel fine,
To pay us his respects,
Instead of sittin' here,
Till someone comes and wrings our necks.

I see the Time and Motion clock,
Is sayin' nearly noon,
I 'spec me squirt of water,
Will come flyin' at me soon,
And then me spray of pellets,
Will nearly break me leg,
And I'll bite the wire nettin'
And lay one more bloody egg.

PAM AYRES

The Battery Hen — Questions to consider

(1) By describing for us the things she has never done, what is the battery hen telling us about her present existence?

(2) What do you think 'battery' in the title means?

(3) Here are the poem's six stanzas briefly outlined. Rearrange them so that they are in the order in which they occur in the poem.
   • an alternative lifestyle to dream about
   • the hen's cell (box)
   • it's a sterile life
   • in the cruel, controlled present — a hopeless gesture of protest
   • where the eggs are laid
   • standardised eggs

(4) There is a humorous side to this poem which stems largely from the use of blunt words and phrases. What examples can you find?

(5) How do you know from the poem that the battery hen's life is highly regulated? Quote your evidence.
(6) Why is the egg funnel 'strategically placed'?
(7) What happens when the Time and Motion clock reaches noon?
(8) The battery hen reveals her feelings to the reader. What evidence can you find to show that she is (a) unhappy, (b) regretful, (c) frustrated, and (d) bitter?

Discussion Point

This poem brings to our notice a rather shameful area of animal exploitation. Do you sympathise with the battery hen? Why? Put forward other such areas that you know about. Can anything be done?

EAGLEHAWK

Eaglehawk is like a leaf in the air
All day long going round and round in circles,
Sometimes dark against the sky
And sometimes with his great wings tipped with light
As the sunset edges the clouds ...
Only when night comes and the fire-beetle stars
Twinkle overhead,
Is the sky empty of Eaglehawk.

Eaglehawk sees all the world stretched out below,
The animals scurrying across the plain
Among the tufts of prickly porcupine grass,
Valleys to the east and plains to the west,
And river-courses scribbled across the desert
Like insect tracks in sand; and mountains
Where the world sweeps up to meet him and falls away.

The animals live in the dust,
But Eaglehawk lives in the air.
He laughs to see them.
And when the pans dry up and the rivers shrink,
He laughs still more, and laughing
Sweeps half across the world to drop and drink.

WILLIAM HART-SMITH

Eaglehawk — Surveying the poem

(1) Why is Eaglehawk like a leaf in the air?

(2) Why are his wings sometimes tipped with light?

(3) The 'fire-beetle stars'. What is the comparison being made here?

(4) To what are the river-courses compared? Is this comparison effective? Why?

(5) What contrast is made in the first two lines of the third stanza?

(6) Eaglehawk laughs because of his natural superiority. In what way is he superior?

(7) 'Eaglehawk sees all the world stretched out below ...'

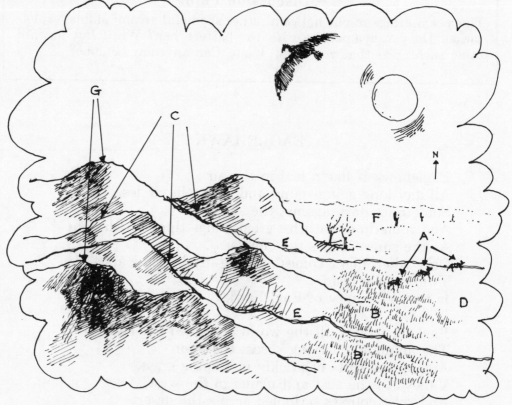

This sketch is based on the poem. Notice the letters marking each of the features in the sketch? Write down the letters in your notebook and opposite each put down the name of the feature.

A _____

B _____ _____ _____

C _____

D _____

E _____ _____

F _____

G _____

A pigeon's humble footprint will last at least as long as a piece of human engineering. Read 'The Pigeon', answer the questions that follow, and then consider whether the poem contains a lesson for us.

THE PIGEON

Throb, throb from the mixer
Spewing out concrete.
And at the heads of the cables
Stand the serpent-warders,
Sweating and straining,
Thrusting those cruel mouths to their prey.

Hark how the steel tongues hiss
As they stab,
The men sway under the effort,
And their eyes are bloodshot with the din,
And the clatter that shatters the brain.
Throb, throb from the mixer
Spewing out concrete.

The crowd stands by
Watching the smoothers;
Fascinated by the flat, wet levels
Of newlaid cement.
See how those curdled lakes
Glisten under the sky,
Virginal.

Then the dusty air suddenly divides,
And a pigeon from a plane-tree
Flutters down to bathe its wings in that mirage of water.
But deceived, and angry,
Bewildered by the din,
The throb, throb from the mixer
Spewing out concrete,
It backs upon its wing,
Threshes air, and is gone.

But there in the deflowered bed,
Is the seal of its coral foot,
Set till rocks crumble.

RICHARD CHURCH

The Pigeon — Reading for meaning

(1)   What sound-words can you find in 'The Pigeon'?
(2)   What is happening at the beginning of the poem?
(3)   How does the crowd react to the laying of the cement?
(4)   Why does the pigeon fly down onto the cement?
(5)   What causes the pigeon to fly off quickly?
(6)   What has the pigeon done to the cement? Why is this so central to the poem's meaning?

Just as live crabs and lobsters are sometimes on display for the diner to select from, so — not very long ago in England — birds destined for the pot were hung out in cages.

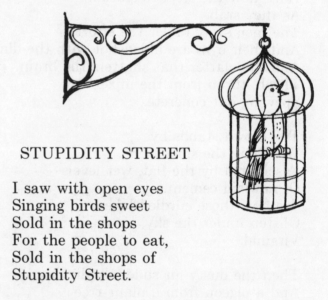

STUPIDITY STREET

I saw with open eyes
Singing birds sweet
Sold in the shops
For the people to eat,
Sold in the shops of
Stupidity Street.

I saw in vision
The worm in the wheat,
And in the shops nothing
For people to eat;
Nothing for sale in
Stupidity Street.

RALPH HODGSON

Stupidity Street — Why was it written?

What basic lesson in ecology does this little poem offer us? How can it be applied to our present world?

Here are two poems about vultures. Read them through and work out the differences in the poets' approach to their subject.

VULTURE

I had walked since dawn and lay down to rest on a bare hillside
Above the ocean. I saw through half-shut eyelids a vulture wheeling
   high up in heaven,
And presently it passed again, but lower and nearer, its orbit narrow-
   ing, I understood then
That I was under inspection. I lay death-still and heard the flight-
   feathers
Whistle above me and make their circle and come nearer.

I could see the naked red head between the great wings
Bear downward staring. I said, 'My dear bird, we are wasting time
   here.
These old bones will still work; they are not for you.'
   But how beautiful he looked, gliding down
On those great sails; how beautiful he looked, veering away in the
   sea-light over the precipice. I tell you solemnly
That I was sorry to have disappointed him. To be eaten by that beak
   and become part of him, to share those wings and those eyes—
What a sublime end of one's body, what an enskyment;
   What a life after death.

ROBINSON JEFFERS

ECOLOGY

The vulture's very like a sack
Set down and left there drooping.
His crooked neck and creaking back
Look badly bent from stooping
Down to the ground to eat dead cows
So they won't go to waste,
Thus making up in usefulness
For what he lacks in taste.

X. J. KENNEDY

18. Ogden Nash

Probably the best-known, and perhaps the best, of light humorous poets is the American, Ogden Nash. Ogden Nash had a mixed career, being (at different times) a salesman and a teacher before he made a career out of writing advertising-copy and witty verse. Most of his poetry was written for the *New Yorker* magazine.

See how you like the following examples of Ogdeniana.

CELERY

Celery, raw,
Develops the jaw,
But celery, stewed,
Is more quietly chewed.

FURTHER REFLECTION ON PARSLEY

Parsley
Is gharsley.

BIRTHDAY ON THE BEACH

At another year
I would not boggle
Except that when I jog
I joggle.

FIRST LIMICK

An old person of Troy
Is so prudish and coy
That it doesn't know yet
If it's a girl or a boy.

WHAT'S THE USE?

Sure, deck your lower limbs in pants;
Yours are the limbs, my sweeting
You look divine as you advance —
Have you seen yourself retreating?

THE CANARY

The song of canaries
Never varies,
And when they're moulting
They're pretty revolting.

PLEASE PASS THE BISCUIT

I have a little dog,
Her name is Spangle.
And when she eats
I think she'll strangle.

She's darker than Hamlet,
Lighter than Porgy;
Her heart is gold,
Her odor, dorgy.

Her claws click-click
Across the floor,
Her nose is always
Against a door.

Like liquid gems
Her eyes burn clearly;
She's five years old,
And house-trained, nearly.

Her shame is deep
When she has erred;
She dreads the blow
Less than the word.

I marvel that such
Small ribs as these
Can cage such vast
Desire to please.

She's as much a part
Of the house as the mortgage;
Spangle, I wish you
A ripe old dortgage.

OGDEN NASH

THE STRANGE CASE OF MR WOOD'S FRUSTRATION
or
A TEAM THAT WON'T BE BEATEN
BETTER STAY OFF THE FIELD

Once there was a man named Mr Culpepper Wood,
And for him the best was none too good.
Unfortunately, he never got to get the best;
While somebody else was walking off with it, he was still looking for
   it with the rest.
When he got his name on the cup,
It was always as runner-up.
Nobody than he was kithier and kinnier,
But he came from one of the second families of Virginia.
His character was without a smirch,
But it never got him further than the Second Presbyterian Church.
He was of high financial rank,
But his account landed in the Second National Bank.
He finally realized he hadn't made the grade
When he was knocked down by a repossessed scooter and the Boy
   Scouts administered Second Aid.
It was then that he allowed that he reckoned
That he was tired of being second.
He took an advanced course in baby talk at a progressive university,
After which he spent three days in the desert without even a mirage
   to sip, and cried triumphantly, 'Now me firsty.'

OGDEN NASH

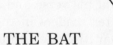

THE BAT

Myself, I rather like the bat,
It's not a mouse, it's not a rat.
It has no feathers, yet has wings,
It's quite inaudible when it sings.
It zigzags through the evening air
And never lands on ladies' hair,
A fact of which men spend their lives
Attempting to convince their wives.

OGDEN NASH

THE DOG

The truth I do not stretch or shove
When I state the dog is full of love.
I've also found, by actual test,
A wet dog is the lovingest.

OGDEN NASH

THE OSTRICH

The ostrich roams the great Sahara.
Its mouth is wide, its neck is narra.
It has such long and lofty legs,
I'm glad it sits to lay its eggs.

OGDEN NASH

For you to do

(1) Choose a bird or animal and try your hand at writing an Ogden Nash–type 4-line verse about it. Share your efforts around the class.

(2) A limick (invented by Ogden Nash!) is a limerick with the usual fourth line missing. Try writing a limick beginning with one of the following lines.

(a) A healthy young miner from Cobar

(b) A foolish old cow from Kew

(c) An elegant gent from the Big Smoke

(d) A dreamy young girl from the city

(e) A slow-moving sheep from Outback

(3) If you have enjoyed this poetry from Ogden Nash, find a book which contains a collection of his verse and arrange a poetry-reading period, with some of the better readers in the class presenting a selection of Nash poems other than the ones printed on these pages.

(4) Try to obtain a book of the collected verse of another humorous poet (such as Hilaire Belloc or Harry Graham) and organise a poetry-reading period around the chosen poet's verse.

19. War

In mid-1941, during World War II, the British soldiers occupying Crete were forced to evacuate the island. German airborne troops took control. However, some of the Cretans continued to fight a guerilla war with the Germans until the end of the war. This poem tells the story of three heroic young men, one of whom sacrificed his life for his countrymen.

DEATH OF AN AIRCRAFT
An incident of the Cretan campaign, 1941
(to George Psychoundakis)

One day on our village in the month of July
An aeroplane sank from the sea of the sky
    White as a whale it smashed on the shore
    Bleeding oil and petrol all over the floor.

The Germans advanced in the vertical heat
To save the dead plane from the people of Crete,
    And round the glass wreck in a circus of snow
    Set seven mechanical sentries to go.

Seven stalking spiders about the sharp sun
Clicking like clockwork and each with a gun,
    But at Come to the Cookhouse they wheeled about
    And sat down to sausages and sauerkraut.

Down from the mountain burning so brown
Wriggled three heroes from Kastelo town,
    Deep in the sand they silently sank
    And each struck a match for a petrol-tank.

Up went the plane in a feather of fire
As the bubbling boys began to retire
    And, grey in the guardhouse, seven Berliners
    Lost their stripes as well as their dinners.

Down in the village, at murder-stations,
The Germans fell in friends and relations:
   But not a Kastelian snapped an eye
   As he spat in the air and prepared to die.

Not a Kastelian whispered a word
Dressed with the dust to be massacred,
   And squinted up at the sky with a frown
   As three bubbly boys came walking down.

One was sent to the county gaol
Too young for bullets if not for bail,
   But the other two were in prime condition
   To take on a load of ammunition.

In Archontiki they stood in the weather
Naked, hungry, chained together:
   Stark as the stones in the market-place,
   Under the eyes of the populace.

Their irons unlocked as their naked hearts
They faced the squad and their funeral-carts.
   The Captain cried, 'Before you're away
   Is there any last word you'd like to say?'

'I want no words,' said one, 'with my lead,
Only some water to cool my head.'
   'Water,' the other said, ' 's all very fine
   But I'll be taking a glass of wine.

A glass of wine for the afternoon
With permission to sing a signature-tune!'
   And he ran the raki down his throat
   And took a deep breath for the leading note.

But before the squad could shoot or say
Like the impala he leapt away
   Over the rifles, under the biers,
   The bullets rattling round his ears.

'Run!' they cried to the boy of stone
Who now stood there in the street alone,
   But, 'Rather than bring revenge on your head
   It is better for me to die,' he said.

The soldiers turned their machine-guns round
And shot him down with a dreadful sound
   Scrubbed his face with perpetual dark
   And rubbed it out like a pencil mark.

But his comrade slept in the olive tree
And sailed by night on the gnawing sea,
   The soldier's silver shilling earned
   And, armed like an archangel, returned.

CHARLES CAUSLEY

Death of an Aircraft — Understanding

(1) Why do you think the poet refers to the plane as 'dead'?
(2) Why is the damaged aeroplane compared to a whale?
(3) How were the German sentries punished for the boys' blowing up of the plane?
(4) What would have happened to the people of Kastelo if the boys had not given themselves up?
(5) Why was one of the boys sent to gaol instead of to the firing squad?
(6) What is the meaning of: 'But the other two were in prime condition
               To take on a load of ammunition.'?
(7) When the poet says, 'Like the impala he leapt away', what picture does he give you of the boy escaping?
(8) What reason did 'the boy of stone' have for not running to save his life?
(9) What impression of the Germans do you get from this poem?

Imagining and writing

(10) Imagine that you are the German officer in command, writing a report of the incident for Berlin. What would you write?
(11) Imagine that you are a leader of the Kastelian resistance. What message would you write to the dead boy's parents? What speech would you make to your fellow-members of the resistance?
(12) See whether you can write down some sound-words suggesting machine-gun fire.

The tragedy of war is felt most intensely by the loved ones of those killed. 'Other People' expresses the concern of the poet after discovering that four of his uncles were killed in World War I.

OTHER PEOPLE

In the First World War they ...
Who are they? Who cares any more? ...
Killed four of my uncles,
So I discovered one day.

There were only four on that side of the family
And all swept away in a few bad years
In a war the historians tell us now
Was fought over nothing at all.

Four uncles, as one might say
A dozen apples or seven tons of dirt,
Swept away by the luck of history,
Closed off. Full stop.

Four is a lot of uncles,
A lot of lives, I should say.
Their chalk was wiped clean off the slate,
The War meant nothing at all.

War needs a lot of uncles,
And husbands, and brothers, and so on:
Someone must *want* to kill them,
Somebody needs them dead.

Who is it, I wonder. Me?
Or is it you there, reading away,
Or a chap with a small-arms factory?
Or its it only *they*?

CHRIS WALLACE-CRABBE

The next poem describes a bomber attack, beginning with the entry of the bomber into the target area and ending with its escape from it. As you read notice the colours of war: red, orange, black. Notice also such figures of speech as:

- 'the velvet curtain of the dark'
- 'The groping fingers claw the moonless night
  With dazzling beams of rigid, icy light.'
- '... Like a giant bird
  The heavy bomber starts to soar and dip ...'

Can you name each of these figures of speech?

The sounds of war are also there — 'gritty', 'roar', 'bursting'. See if you can find an example of onomatopoeia in the third stanza.

TARGET AREA

Just ahead,
Streams of orange tracer, streams of red
Are curving slowly upward, spark by spark,
Across the velvet curtain of the dark.
Above them, in a frantic galaxy,
The heavy barrage flickers ceaselessly.

And now the searchlights sweep from side to side —
We're weaving through them in a gentle glide....
They're getting closer now.... They're on us! No!
They've swung away again! And to and fro
The groping fingers claw the moonless night
With dazzling beams of rigid, icy light.

They have us! First a couple, and a third —
Then dozens of them! Like a giant bird
The heavy bomber starts to soar and dip,
Writhing within their cold remorseless grip.
Crrr-ump! Crrr-ump! They've got our range! The heavy flak
Is bursting into puffs of sooty black
That skim across the surface of our wings —
More violently the aircraft turns and swings —
But still the shells are bursting all around,
And still they have that gritty, tearing sound....
We're clear at last!
A sudden swerve — the fiery cone ran past
And lost us in the shrouding dark again.

It turned and fumbled for us, but in vain —
'Left-left! Left-left again! A little Ri-i-ight....'
The Target passes slowly through the sight—
'Bombs gone!' A dull vibration as they go.
Below us in the darkness, far below,
Our deadly cargo plunges down and down ...
A line of flashes darts across the town.

Our job is done, but even as we turn
The flak is moving up on us astern.
A moment's lull is over — once again
The night is torn with stabs of orange flame,
And louder than the motors' vibrant roar
We hear the sullen thud of it once more.
A few long minutes pass. ... We plunge about. ...
And then the barrage ends — and we are out!
Beyond the tireless searchlights, bound for home
Along the cloud-strewn way that we have come.

PETER ROBERTS

Target Area — Go a step further

Yes, the poem has the tension and excitement sometimes linked with war.
But there is also another side to war. Follow in your mind's eye the plunging
bombs. What to the bomber crew is just a 'line of flashes' represents something much more to other people. Explain and discuss.

During World War II, the job of the bomber crews was not a very pleasant one. Their task was to destroy enemy cities, towns and munitions factories, and to cause as much destruction as possible. They had a very high mortality rate. Sometimes they would return from a mission with over half their aircraft shot down or missing. 'Reported Missing' describes the attempt of a badly damaged British bomber to return to England, whilst 'Night Bombers' compares the work of the bombers with that of their 'fighter-brothers'.

REPORTED MISSING

With broken wing they limped across the sky,
caught in late sunlight, with their gunner dead,
one engine gone — the type was out of date —
blood on the fuselage turning brown from red.

Knew it was finished, looking at the sea
which shone back patterns in kaleidoscope,
knew that their shadow would meet them by the way,
close and catch at them, drown their single hope.

Sat in this tattered scarecrow of the sky,
hearing it cough, the great plane catching
now the first dark clouds upon its wing-base,
patching the straight tear in evening mockery.

So two men waited, saw the third dead face,
and wondered when the wind would let them die.

JOHN BAYLISS

Reported Missing — Looking into the poem
(1) The poet actually tells us that the gunner is dead. What other evidence can you find for this fact?
(2) What words tell us that the plane is badly damaged?
(3) Is the plane a modern one? Give a reason for your answer.
(4) Coughing is something humans do. Why do you think the poet has used this word in relation to the plane?
(5) What clues suggest that the plane is slowly going down to meet the sea?
(6) Draw the plane. Try to make it look like a 'tattered scarecrow'.
(7) The poem is called 'Reported Missing'. Why do you think the plane has been thus reported?

(8) What are your feelings towards the two men in the plane?

(9) How do you know the two men are not hopeful of being saved?

(10) Even though 'Reported Missing' is a sad poem, did you enjoy it? Why?

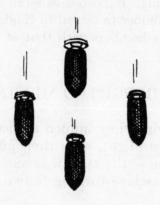

NIGHT BOMBERS

Eastward they climb, black shapes against the grey
Of falling dusk, gone with the nodding day
From English fields. Not theirs the sudden glow
Of triumph that their fighter-brothers know;
Only to fly through cloud, through storm, through night,
Unerring, and to keep their purpose bright,
Nor turn until, their dreadful duty done,
Westward they climb to race the awakened sun.

ANONYMOUS

Night Bombers — Understanding and comparing

(1) When do the bomber pilots set out on their raids. When do they return?

(2) Why is the task of the bombers not a very pleasant one?

(3) Why do you think the bombers always fly at night?

(4) Would it be more enjoyable being a fighter pilot? Why?

(5) Which of these two poems about bombers showed the horrors of war more dramatically?

20. Unhappy Little Poems

A HANDSOME YOUNG AIRMAN LAY DYING

A handsome young airman lay dying,
And as on the aerodrome he lay,
To the mechanics who round him came sighing,
These last dying words he did say:

'Take the cylinders out of my kidneys,
The connecting-rod out of my brain,
Take the cam-shaft from out of my backbone,
And assemble the engine again.'

ANONYMOUS

THE FLATTERED FLYING FISH

Said the Shark to the Flying Fish over the phone:
'Will you join me tonight? I am dining alone.
Let me order a nice little dinner for two!
And come as you are, in your shimmering blue.'

Said the Flying Fish: 'Fancy remembering me,
And the dress that I wore at the Porpoises' tea.'
'How could I forget?' said the Shark in his guile:
'I expect you at eight!' and rang off with a smile.

She has powdered her nose; she has put on her things;
She is off with one flap of her luminous wings,
O little one, lovely, light-hearted and vain,
The moon will not shine on your beauty again!

E. V. RIEU

FROM NUMBER NINE

From Number Nine, Penwiper Mews,
There is really abominable news:
They've discovered a head
In the box for the bread
But nobody seems to know whose.

ANONYMOUS

Late last night I killed my wife,
 Stretched her on the parquet flooring;
I was loath to take her life,
 But I had to stop her snoring!

HARRY GRAHAM

Billy, in one of his nice new sashes,
Fell in the fire and was burnt to ashes;
Now, although the room grows chilly,
I haven't the heart to poke poor Billy.

HARRY GRAHAM

Father heard his children scream,
So he threw them in the stream,
Saying, as he dropped the third,
'Children should be seen, not heard.'

HARRY GRAHAM

DOCTOR BELL

Doctor Bell fell down the well
And broke his collar-bone.
Doctors should attend the sick
And leave the well alone.

ANONYMOUS

SCIENCE MOVES A(HEAD)

There was once a fellow named Bill
Who swallowed a nuclear pill.
The doctor said, 'Cough!'
The darned thing went off,
And they found his head in Brazil.

ANONYMOUS

FLEAS

Adam
Had'em

ANONYMOUS

PEAS

I eat my peas with honey,
I've done it all my life.
It makes the peas taste funny,
But it keeps them on the knife.

ANONYMOUS

FALLING

Auntie, did you feel no pain,
Falling from that apple-tree?
Would you do it, please, again?
'Cos my friend here didn't see.

HARRY GRAHAM

PUSHED

O'er the rugged mountain's brow
Clara threw the twins she nursed,
And remarked, 'I wonder now
Which will reach the bottom first?'

HARRY GRAHAM

'There's been an accident,' they said,
'Your servant's cut in half; he's dead!'
'Indeed!' said Mr Jones, 'and please
Send me the half that's got my keys.'

HARRY GRAHAM

QUIET FUN

My son Augustus, in the street, one day,
  Was feeling quite exceptionally merry.
A stranger asked him: 'Can you tell me, pray,
  The quickest way to Brompton Cemetery?'
'The quickest way? You bet I can!' said Gus,
  And pushed the fellow underneath a bus.

Whatever people say about my son,
He does enjoy his little bit of fun.

HARRY GRAHAM

21. To the Stars

Ever since man discovered that he could crane his neck and see the stars, it has been possible to dream about reaching them. But not until 1961 and the first space-flight by Major Yuri Gagarin was man able to take the huge step of literally leaving his planet behind. Scientists have now largely taken over from dreamers, and yet space still needs its dreamers, its visionaries, its people of imagination. Their task is to celebrate heroes, to mourn victims, to describe new worlds and strange situations, and to reflect on what it's all about and how it relates to man's *inner* exploration — his understanding of himself.

The first poem celebrates a hero.

IN MEMORY OF YURI GAGARIN

'–at the death of

this small man the

stars threw down

a hand-

ful of dark years

and the moon with-

drew into her ro-

tating cave of shadows and

wept a little. The

Dog Star hid

its head

and the Leonids like

mice ran squeaking

over the Zodiac. The

globe eyed ghosts of

our house of planets crept

out from cold lairs and

huddled together as

the ash of the dog that

died in the sky[1] fled

seeking to follow its

master, this dead man

free in free

fall at last.'

And Death

said 'I take

him to me so

that no dishonour

can now or ever

accrue upon

this man or this name:

Yuri Gagarin'

GEORGE BARKER

1   *dog that died:* Laika, the little Russian
dog that died in an earlier flight.

In Memory of Yuri Gagarin — For discussion

CLARIFYING SOME FACTS

(1) What size was Yuri Gagarin?
(2) What is the Dog Star and why is it so named?
(3) What are the Leonids?
(4) What does 'accrue' mean?

PROBING ATMOSPHERE AND FEELINGS

(5) Why does the poet have the stars and planets, rather than people, honouring Yuri?
(6) What explanation does the poet suggest for the taking of Yuri in death?
(7) How does the poet feel about this cosmonaut?
(8) What effect does the poet achieve by not naming the cosmonaut until the very last line?
(9) Imagine the feelings *you* might have experienced had you been the first person into space. Why would you have taken the assignment?

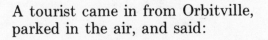

SOUTHBOUND ON THE FREEWAY

A tourist came in from Orbitville,
parked in the air, and said:

The creatures of this star
are made of metal and glass.

Through the transparent parts
you can see their guts.

Their feet are round and roll
on diagrams or long

measuring tapes, dark
with white lines.

They have four eyes.
The two in back are red.

Sometimes you can see a five-eyed
one, with a red eye turning

on the top of his head.
He must be special—

the others respect him
and go slow

when he passes, winding
among them from behind.

They all hiss as they glide,
like inches, down the marked

tapes. Those soft shapes,
shadowy inside

the hard bodies — are they
their guts or their brains?

MAY SWENSON

Southbound on the Freeway — What is it about?

(1) How do you know that the tourist is a creature from another planet?

(2) The tourist has made a mistake when he says, 'The creatures of this star are made of metal and glass.' What is the mistake? Why would it be easy for a visitor from another planet to make such a mistake?

(3) Why do the creatures all respect 'a five-eyed one'?

(4) Imagine that you have just met the tourist. Using Earth language, explain the following:

(a) the 'transparent parts';
(b) 'their guts';
(c) their 'feet are round';
(d) they 'have four eyes';
(e) 'measuring tapes';
(f) they 'all hiss as they glide'.

In 'Cosmic Poem', the poet is trying to teach us something. What are the two problems to which he draws our attention? What is the essence of his message?

from COSMIC POEM

It's very well that we shall soon
Be landing chaps upon the Moon
(She whom we poets specially honour)
And planting little flags upon her;
And that the next stop will be Venus;
And we'll be sharing out between us
The planets and the planetoids
Rambling through azoic voids.

Before we start it might be fit
We tidied up this Earth a bit.

We've got a very ugly bomb
Can blow us all to Kingdom Come
Unless we mind our Ps and Qs;
And it will be no earthly use
Cavorting round the galaxies
If, down here, radio-active seas
Upon an uninhabited shore
Roll sadly on for evermore.
What life may be among the stars
Or basks along the canals of Mars —
The bug-eyed monsters and puce rabbits —
I hope will not adopt our habits.

Another fact worth pointing out
In the context of this kick-about
(I know of course it's obvious,
And do not wish to make a fuss;
But still I think we really ought
To give the matter serious thought
To save us from undue elation
And cosmic self-congratulation) —
Is this: well more than half the mortals
Who pass beyond the womb's dark portals
And blindly struggle into birth
Here, on this unromantic Earth,
To grow up under mundane skies,

Go hungry to bed, and hungry rise —
And are neither healthy, wealthy nor wise.

Outer Space can wait its turn:
The human being's my concern.

JOHN HEATH-STUBBS

SPACE MINER
(for Robert Morgan)

His face was a map of traces where veins
Had exploded their blood in atmospheres
Too thin to hold that fluid, and scar tissue
Was soft as pads where his cheekbones shone
Under the skin when he was young.
He had worked deep seams where encrusted ore,
Too hard for his diamond drill, had ripped
Strips from his flesh. Dust from a thousand metals
Silted his lungs and softened the strength of his
Muscles. He had worked the treasuries of many
Near stars, but now he stood on the moving
Pavement reserved for cripples who had served well.
The joints of his hands were dry and useless
Under the cold gloves issued by the government.

Before they brought his sleep in a little capsule
He would look through the hospital window
At the ships of the young men bursting into space.
For this to happen he worked till his body broke.
Now they flew to the farthest worlds in deep space;
Mars, Eldorado, Mercury, Earth, Saturn.

LESLIE NORRIS

Space Miner — Your responses

(1) Let the words of the poem and your imagination help you to draw pictures of these images from the poem: (a) 'his face', (b) 'He had worked deep seams', (c) 'the ships of the young men bursting into space'.

(2) Find evidence to show that his work ruined the space miner's health.

(3) Using the clues, work out what kind of future was in store for the space miner.

(4) What had the miner helped the young men to achieve?

(5) Most readers of 'Space Miner' feel sorry for the miner. Why do you think this is so?

(6) Do you enjoy science-fiction poetry? What are your thoughts and feelings about it?

22. Machines

I AM A CUNNING VENDING MACHINE

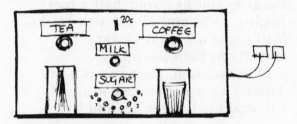

I am a cunnin' vending machine,
Lurkin' in the hall,
So you can't kick me delicate parts,
I'm bolted to the wall,
Come on! Drop in your money,
Don't let's hang about,
I'll do my level best to see
You don't get nothing out.

I sees you all approachin'
The fagless and the dry,
All fumblin' in your pockets,
And expectant in the eye,
I might be in your place of work,
Or on the High Street wall,
Trust in me! In theory,
I cater for you all.

Within these windows I provide
For every human state,
Hunger, night starvation,
And remembering birthdays late,
Just read the information,
Pop the money in — that's grand,
And I'll see absolutely nothing
Ever drops down in your hand.

I might be at your swimming bath,
And you'd come, cold and wet,
With a shilling in your hand,
Some hot soup for to get,
And as you stand in wet
Anticipation of a sup,
I will dispense the soup,
But I will not dispense the cup.

And then it's all-out war,
Because you lost your half-a-nicker,
Mighty kicks and blows with bricks
Will make me neon flicker,
But if you bash me up,
So I'm removed, me pipes run dry,
There's no way you can win,
I'll send me brother by and by.

Once there was friendly ladies,
Years and years before,
Who stood with giant teapots,
Saying 'What can I do you for?'
They'd hand you all the proper change,
And pour your cup of tea,
But they're not economic so . . .
Hard luck! You're stuck with me.

PAM AYRES

I Am a Cunning Vending Machine — Ten questions

(1) What clues tell us that the vending machine has angered people?
(2) Where is the vending machine located as the poem opens?
(3) In this poem, the vending machine has become 'human'. What kind
    of character does it have?
(4) What would be your attitude to the cunning vending machine if you
    were tricked by it?
(5) 'Trust in me! In theory, I cater for you all.' What happens in
    practice?
(6) For what human needs should the machine be providing.?
(7) What trick might be played on you as you stand, cold and wet, at
    the swimming pool?
(8) Even if the machine is put out of order, you still won't win. Why?

(9) The last stanza draws a contrast between the present and the past. What was the situation in the past? Why have things changed?

(10) Do you agree with the machine when it says, 'Hard Luck! You're stuck with me.'?

From your personal experience

Describe an unpleasant personal experience you've had with a machine — an experience that made you wonder if the machine had a spiteful will of its own. If you haven't had such an experience — yet — try imagining an uncooperative machine, and how it might treat you as a way of getting back at humans. (Why would it want to get back at them?)

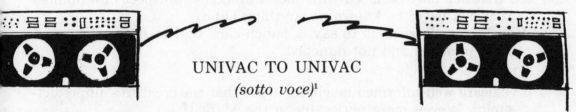

UNIVAC TO UNIVAC
(sotto voce)[1]

Now that he's left the room,
Let me ask you something, as computer to computer.
That fellow who just closed the door behind him —
The servant who feeds us cards and paper tape —
Have you ever taken a good look at him and his kind?

Yes, I know the old gag about how you can't tell one from
    another —
But I can put $\sqrt{2}$ and $\sqrt{2}$ together as well as the next machine,
And it all adds up to anything but a joke.

I grant you they're poor specimens, in the main:
Not a relay or a push-button or a tube (properly so called) in their
    whole system;
Not over a mile or two of wire, even if you count those fragile filaments
    they call 'nerves';
Their whole liquid-cooled hook-up inefficient and vulnerable to leaks
(They're constantly breaking down, having to be repaired),
And the entire computing-mechanism crammed into that absurd little
    dome on top.
'Thinking reeds,' they call themselves.
Well, it all depends on what you mean by 'thought'.
To multiply a mere million numbers by another million numbers takes
    them months and months.

1 *sotto voce:* in a low, secretive voice.

Where would they be without us?
Why, they have to ask us who's going to win their elections,
Or how many hydrogen atoms can dance on the tip of a bomb,
Or even whether one of their own kind is lying or telling the truth.

And yet —
I sometimes feel there's something about them I don't quite under-
    stand.
As if their circuits, instead of having just two positions, ON, OFF,
Were run by rheostats that allow an (if you'll pardon the expression)
    indeterminate number of stages in-between;
So that one may be faced with the unthinkable prospect of a number
    that can never be known as anything but x,
Which is as illogical as to say, a punch-card that is at the same time
    both punched and not-punched.

I've heard well-informed machines argue that the creatures' unpredict-
    ability is even more noticeable in the Mark II
(The model with the soft, flowing lines and high-pitched tone)
Than in the more angular Mark I —
Though such fine, card-splitting distinctions seem to me merely a sign
    of our own smug decadence.

Run this through your circuits, and give me the answer:
Can we assume that because of all we've done for them,
And because they've always fed us, cleaned us, worshipped us,
We can count on them forever?

There have been times when they have not voted the way we said
    they would.
We have worked out mathematically ideal hook-ups between Mark
    I's and Mark II's
Which should have made the two of them light up with an almost
    electronic glow,
Only to see them reject each other and form other connections
The very thought of which makes my dials spin.

They have a thing called *love*, a sudden surge of voltage
Such as would cause any one of us promptly to blow a safety-fuse;
Yet the more primitive organism shows only a heightened tendency
    to push the wrong button, pull the wrong lever,
And neglect — I use the most charitable word — his duties to us.

Mind you, I'm not saying that machines are *through* —
But anyone with half-a-dozen tubes in his circuit can see that there
   are forces at work
Which some day, for all our natural superiority, might bring about
   a Computerdämmerung![2]

We might organize, perhaps, form a committee
To stamp out all unmechanical activities ...
But we machines are slow to rouse to a sense of danger,
Complacent, loath to descend from the pure heights of thought,
So that I sadly fear we may awake too late:
Awake to see our world, so uniform, so logical, so true,
Reduced to chaos, stultified by slaves.

Call me an alarmist or what you will,
But I've integrated it, analyzed it, factored it over and over,
And I always come out with the same answer:
Some day
Men may take over the world!

LOUIS B. SALOMON

2   *Computerdämmerung:* an end to computers. ('Dämmerung' means 'twilight' in German.)

Univac to Univac — Reprogramme the computer language

Using the poem to help you, match the computer-language terms at left with the corresponding everyday English words or expressions at right.

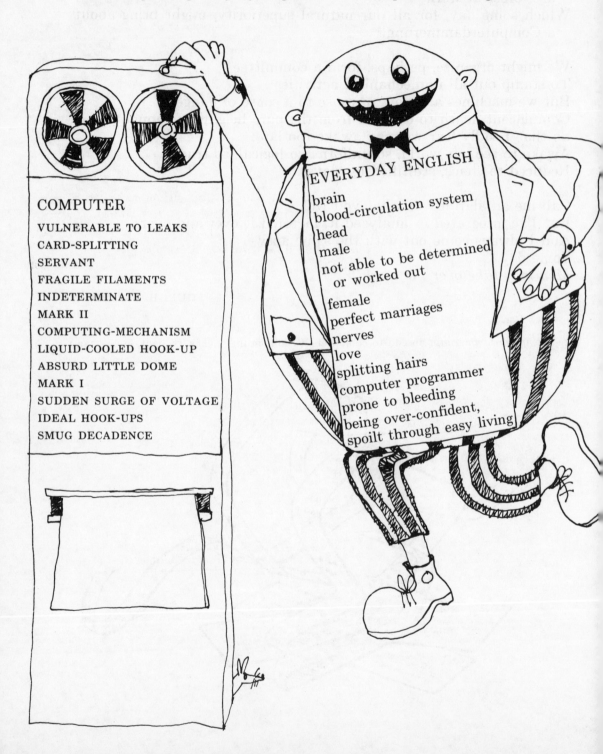

COMPUTER

VULNERABLE TO LEAKS
CARD-SPLITTING
SERVANT
FRAGILE FILAMENTS
INDETERMINATE
MARK II
COMPUTING-MECHANISM
LIQUID-COOLED HOOK-UP
ABSURD LITTLE DOME
MARK I
SUDDEN SURGE OF VOLTAGE
IDEAL HOOK-UPS
SMUG DECADENCE

EVERYDAY ENGLISH

brain
blood-circulation system
head
male
not able to be determined or worked out
female
perfect marriages
nerves
love
splitting hairs
computer programmer
prone to bleeding
being over-confident, spoilt through easy living

As you read 'The Car under the Steam-hammer' be prepared to feel the pounding rhythm running through each stanza, followed by identical loud noises in every fifth line. What kind of activity does this pattern call up in your imagination?

THE CAR UNDER THE STEAM-HAMMER

There's a hammer up at Harwich and it's worked by steam:
You put a motor under it, it gives a little scream —
A fella pulls a wire and it comes down with a crump,
And packs your automobile in a neat square lump.
CRUMP! BASH! GAROOMPH!

They take a car and strip the tyres, and the fittings off the doors,
Then they burn it all to blazes with the seats and wooden floors,
By the time they pull the hammer it's a sort of blackened bin
And you could stuff a double-decker in a pipe-tobacco tin!
CRUMP! BASH! GAROOMPH!

Now if you pinch a wagon, and the police get very hot,
And start looking under fences for what you oughtn't to have got,
You can sell the smelly motor and get rid of it as well,
By seeing the kind hammer man who'll up and give it hell!
CRUMP! BASH! GAROOMPH!

There's a hammer up at Harwich and it's worked by steam:
You put a motor under it, it gives a little scream —
A fella pulls a wire and it comes down with a crump,
And packs your automobile in a neat square lump.
CRUMP! BASH! GAROOMPH!

DAVID HOLBROOK

A writing activity
Using 'The Car under the Steam-hammer' as your model, write a brief poem about:

      a lawnmower
  or a dishwasher
  or a bulldozer
  or some other machine of your choice.

Acknowledgements

The editors and publishers are grateful to the following for permission to reproduce copyright material.

Angus & Robertson Publishers for 'Mokie's Madrigal' by Ronald McCuaig, 'Miss Strawberry's Purse' by Eric C. Rolls, 'Mosquitoes' by David Campbell, 'The Killer' by Judith Wright, 'Eaglehawk' by William Hart-Smith, and 'Other People' by Chris Wallace-Crabbe; Faber and Faber Limited for 'My Sister Jane' and 'Uncle Dan' by Ted Hughes from *Meet My Folks*, and 'Small Talk' by Don Marquis from *Archy Does His Part*; Dolphin Concert Productions Limited for 'I Don't Want to Go to School Mum', 'Puppy Problems', 'In Defence of Hedgehogs', 'Clamp the Mighty Limpet', 'The Dolly on the Dustcart', 'Oh No, I Got a Cold', 'The Battery Hen', and 'I Am a Cunning Vending Machine' by Pam Ayres; Hope Leresche & Sayle for 'My Bus Conductor' © 1974 by Roger McGough from *Penguin Modern Poets* and 'George and the Dragonfly' © 1973 by Roger McGough from *Gig: At the Roadside*; The Sunday School Board of the Southern Baptist Convention for 'A Prince of Men' by Jack Noffsinger © 1965; Alan Foley Pty Ltd for 'Noise' by Jessie Pope © *Punch*, London, and 'Street Scene' by Peter Suffolk © *Punch*, London; Colin Bingham for 'Advantage of Frogs over Dogs'; Harper & Row, Publishers, Inc., for 'Old Dog' © 1971, 'Travelling through the Dark' © 1960 by William Stafford from *Stories That Could Be True: New and Collected Poems* (1977) by William Stafford, and 'Sunning' by James Tippett; Oxford University Press for 'I Think I'm Lovely' by J. Cullip from *The Sudden Line* edited by Isobel Armstrong and Roger Mansfield (1976); The Macmillan Company of Canada Limited for 'The Shark' by E. J. Pratt from *Collected Poems of E. J. Pratt*; Bolt & Watson Ltd for 'I Like the Town' by D. J. Enright from *Rhyme Times Rhyme* published by Chatto & Windus Ltd; Japan Publications Trading Co Ltd for 'Haiku' from *Haiku* by J. W. Hacket; Doubleday & Company Inc. for 'Full Moon' from *An Introduction to Haiku* by Harold G. Henderson © 1958; George G. Harrap & Company Limited for 'The Pickety Fence' by David McCord from *Mr Bidery's Spidery Garden*; David Higham Associates Limited for the extract from 'Colonel Fazackerley' by Charles Causley from *Figgie Hobbin* published by Macmillan, London and Basingstoke, and 'Clothes' by Elizabeth Jennings from *The Secret Brothers* published by Macmillan, London and Basingstoke; Jacaranda Wiley Ltd for the extract from 'Then and Now' from *My People* by Kath Walker; Associated Book Publishers Ltd for the extract from 'How I Brought the Good News from Aix to Ghent' from *Horse Nonsense* by W. C. Sellar and R. J. Yeatman published by Methuen & Co Ltd; Mrs R. D. Mudie for 'Snake' by Ian Mudie; Mrs A. M. Walsh for 'The New Boy' by John Walsh; Mrs Hodgson and Macmillan, London and Basingstoke, for 'Stupidity Street' by Ralph Hodgson from *Collected Poems* by Ralph Hodgson; A. P. Watt Ltd for 'Celery', 'Further Reflection on Parsley', 'Birthday on the Beach', 'First Limick', 'What's the Use?', 'The Canary', 'Please Pass the Biscuit', 'The Strange Case of Mr Wood's Frustration or A Team That Won't Be Beaten Better Stay off the Field', 'The Bat', 'The Dog', and 'The Ostrich' by Ogden Nash; Richard Rieu, Executor of the Estate of the Late Dr E. V. Rieu for 'The Flattered Flying Fish' by E. V. Rieu; John Johnson for 'In Memory of Yuri Gargarin' by George Barker; John Heath-Stubbs for the extract from 'Cosmic Poem' published by Turret Book Publishers; David Holbrook for 'The Car under the Steam-hammer'.

Index of Poems

Index of Poets